Sensory Modulation

Changing how you feel
through Using Your Senses

Resource Manual

Carolyn Fitzgibbon and Julie O'Sullivan

First published by Sensory Modulation Brisbane 2018

National Library of Australia Cataloguing - in Publication entry:

Julie O 'Sullivan and Carolyn Fitzgibbon, authors

Sensory Modulation, Changing how you feel through Using Your Senses, Resource Manual.

sensory-modulation- Brisbane.com.au

ISBN: 978-0-6482280-1-1 Kindle

ISBN: 978-0-6482280-2-8 Epub

ISBN: 978-0-6482280-3-5 PDF

ISBN: 978-0-6482280-4-2 Print.

ISBN-13: 978-0-6482280-5-9 Print

Editor: Michael Lefcourt, Page Perfect Editing: Corporate and academic editing

Disclaimer:

While the authors have attempted to make the information in this publication as accurate as possible, it is for personal use only and is provided in good faith without any express or implied warranty. There is no representation or warranty made as to the completeness or accuracy of the information in this publication. References to other sources of information (including textbooks and websites) are not endorsed by the authors in any way. The authors take no responsibility for any loss or liability incurred in connection with the use of the published material.

This publication is provided for information purposes only. Information in this publication does not imply endorsement of third party services or products and cannot provide you with individualised health and medical advice. Purchasers use the published material at their own risk, and should always consider if the strategies are appropriate for individual circumstances. Purchasers are encouraged to seek independent advice from a qualified health care professional when needed.

Part 1

Sensory Modulation

Chapter 1:

Introduction

Introduction

Sensory modulation is a therapeutic intervention that engages a person's senses to change how they feel. For many years, occupational therapists have used sensory modulation to help children with autism and intellectual disabilities self-regulate, and adults with dementia to feel calm and safe and engage in meaningful activities like leisure and self-care tasks.

The value of sensory modulation is increasingly recognised in an ever-widening range of settings, including physical and mental health and in the general community. Sensory modulation has been formally acknowledged as effective in improving the quality of mental health service delivery and driving mental health service reform. Many mental health policies and guidelines specifically recommend the implementation of sensory modulation to enhance clinical outcomes and promote recovery and trauma-informed care (Fitzgibbon & O'Sullivan, 2015), including the following two Australian examples:

- The national framework for recovery-oriented mental health services: Guide for practitioners and providers (2013) recommends that clinicians be trained in 'non-forceful therapeutic crisis intervention, including sensory modulation strategies'.
- The Queensland policy statement on reducing and where possible eliminating restraint and seclusion in Queensland mental health services (2008) specifically identifies sensory interventions as a key strategy.

Embedding sensory modulation into core practice has far-reaching benefits for clients, their families and carers, service providers, and organisations in general. Workers in health, community and primary care sectors who enhance their knowledge and active application of sensory modulation can provide immediate and long reaching positive benefits to their practice and workplace.

This manual provides practical assistance for people to increase their knowledge and skills concerning sensory modulation. For ease of use, the manual is divided into four parts, each containing specific chapter content with core themes.

Part 1 contains chapters 1 through to 5 and sets the scene for the use of sensory modulation. Chapter 1 is this introduction. Chapter 2 explains the **origins of sensory modulation in mental health**, including its connection to recovery, self-management and trauma-informed care. Chapter 3 discusses the **eight senses** and provides examples showing how sensory input can be employed to change feelings and reduce stress levels. Chapter 4 explains **how sensory modulation works** by providing a detailed description of the science of sensory modulation that emphasises the power sensations of touch, vestibular/movement, and proprioception. Chapter 5 discusses the concept of a **sensory lens**, and the connection between sensory modulation and the **PEO** (person, environment and occupation) **Model**.

Part 2 of the manual contains chapters 6 through to 12 and focuses on the practical application of sensory modulation principles and techniques. Chapter 6 recommends a working guide to **using sensory modulation safely**. Chapter 7 explores **getting started with sensory modulation**, outlining a formula to help integrate sensory modulation into everyday practice. Chapter 8 introduces the concept of **sensational spaces**, and chapter 9 discusses **sensational activities**. Chapter 10 highlights the role of sensory modulation in addressing **healthy living and lifestyle changes**. Chapter 11 identifies **future opportunities** and directions for sensory modulation in promoting health and wellbeing, and chapter 12 provides some concluding remarks.

Part 3 of the manual contains chapters 13 through 19 and offers a wide range of resources to support the use of sensory modulation. Chapter 13 provides practical 'go to' techniques for **managing specific intense emotions and challenging scenarios**–for example, when managing panic, anger, pain, auditory hallucinations, self-harm, dementia, cravings and improving sleep and feeling grounded. Chapter 14 provides a resource list of a wide range of **sensory modulation equipment and items**, which are divided into the different sensory systems and range from budget to deluxe items. Chapter 15 **defines** the concepts frequently used in reference to sensory modulation. Chapter 16 offers a range of **factsheets and worksheets** to support the use of sensory modulation in practice, on topics such as sensory kits, sensory diets, sensory exploration worksheets, personal safety plans and sensory skills checklists. Chapter 17 is a worksheet called **Leisure Interests and Sport Through the Senses (LISTS)**. Chapter 18 provides a comprehensive **risk management table** for the safe use of sensory modulation in practice, and chapter 19 offers a selection of worksheets to **support the development of sensory spaces**, including information on sensory zones, sensory design and conducting a sensory audit.

All the factsheets, worksheets and tables in this manual are also available to download as a print quality resource.

A key theme throughout the manual is the safe and appropriate use of sensory modulation, and its tailoring for the individual. Safety considerations include the safe use of equipment and the managing of identified risks. Appropriate use of sensory modulation includes using everyday items in everyday places without the need to purchase expensive equipment that many people cannot afford. Each person may respond differently to sensory input, and sensory modulation needs to be tailored to the individual. For a person to be able to quickly change how they feel, it is important for sensory modulation to be available when they need it.

This manual outlines practical strategies for improving access to sensory modulation within hospital, organisational and home environments. It will enable users to build a solid foundation on which to grow practical knowledge and skills concerning sensory modulation, and how to apply these skills so they can work with a diverse range of people. A great strength of sensory modulation is its relevance and applicability to all individuals in everyday life, irrespective of diagnosis, symptoms, behaviours and complexities.

Carolyn and Julie.

Chapter 2:

Origins of Sensory Modulation in Mental Health

Origins of Sensory Modulation in Mental Health

Sensory modulation has long been used by occupational therapists working with a variety of people including children, the elderly and people with intellectual disabilities. In the last decade, its use in adult mental health populations has emerged as a highly valuable, successful and mainstream treatment intervention. As our knowledge of the human brain becomes more sophisticated, so too does our understanding of sensory modulation and sensory processing and how this can positively affect daily functioning.

A better understanding of unique sensory patterns and preferences can not only offer an alternative explanation to particular behaviours seen in mental health clients but also help identify interventions to enhance participation in everyday life, or 'live a satisfying life' (Dunn, 2001). A literature review conducted by Sutton and Nicholson (2011) identified that, for people with mental illness, sensitivity (both over and under) to sensory input is common and can result in the avoidance of situations, the missing of key sensory input, and higher states of arousal and emotional reactivity. Occupational therapists would interpret this observation as reflective of sensory processing patterns, their expertise enabling the sharing of this knowledge to 'bridge the gap' between an individual's sensory needs 'and the activities of interest in their lives' (Dunn, 2001). Champagne and Stromberg (2004) suggest that individuals with a trauma history, mental illness and addictions are often unaware of their particular sensory needs or stress responses. An inability to adequately notice and adjust to sensory input can result in difficulties managing emotions and a decline in areas of occupational performance (Brown, Tollefson, Dunn, Cromwell & Filion, 2001).

Sensory modulation is an evidence-based and highly effective therapeutic intervention to assist individuals in the building of foundational coping skills to manage stress, regulate emotions and enhance occupational functioning. It can be defined as follows:

> *Changing how you feel through using your senses.*
>
> *(Julie O'Sullivan and Carolyn Fitzgibbon, 2013)*

The use of sensory modulation has been shown to

- decrease the need for restraint and seclusion and promote the adoption of trauma-informed care practices (Champagne & Stromberg, 2004)
- be an effective alternative to more coercive practices, support self-regulation skills and foster trust and rapport-building between clinicians and clients (Sutton & Nicholson, 2011)
- support a recovery-oriented approach (Fitzgibbon & O'Sullivan, 2015).

Sensory modulation works by *changing how a person feels* through sensory input. This sensory input changes the physiology of the body, and in doing so creates a shift in how the person feels.

Sensory modulation is broader than just aiming to feel calm and relaxed. It can also be used to

- ***ground:*** when feeling dissociated, spacey or having difficulty focusing on the present
- ***soothe:*** when feeling self-hatred, shame, sad or anxious
- ***calm:*** when feeling anxious, scared, angry or agitated
- ***relax:*** when the muscles feel tense or the mind feels stressed
- ***alert:*** when feeling lethargic, tired or sedated, or having trouble concentrating
- ***reduce or intensify sensations:*** when feeling self-hatred or shame or the urge to self-harm

- ***increase pleasure:*** when feeling the need for joy in the moment or happy memories from the past
- ***create a sense of safety:*** when feeling unsafe, triggered by the current environment or past memories
- ***self-manage symptoms:*** when experiencing auditory hallucinations, panic attacks, or insomnia
- ***manage pain and itch:*** when chronic pain or itch is an issue
- ***cope with grief and shock:*** through soothing the body and mind
- ***cope with cravings for addictions:*** through using alternatives to substances
- ***reminisce:*** when wanting to improve memory or connect an elderly person to familiar or pleasurable sensations.

Sensory modulation, recovery and self-management

The connection between sensory modulation, recovery and self-management becomes increasingly evident with analysis and exploration of these concepts.

In Australia, The national framework for recovery-oriented mental health services (2013) provides an 'understanding and approach to recovery-oriented mental health service delivery'. The document defines recovery as 'being able to create and live a meaningful and contributing life in a community of choice with or without the presence of mental health issues'. Therefore recovery 'involves the development of new meaning and purpose in one's life as one grows beyond the catastrophic effects of mental illness' (Anthony, 1993). A distinction between clinical and personal recovery is made in some of the literature, with exploration of their interconnectedness. Glover (2012) suggests that while clinical and personal recovery are separate concepts, 'one without the other remains incomplete'. Key elements outlined in the framework which highlight the relationship between clinical and personal recovery include the fostering of personal responsibility, promoting shared decision-making and supporting the development of self-management and self-empowerment Researchers, service users and service providers generally agree that while recovery means much more than symptom improvement, the reduction or alleviation of distress associated with symptoms as well as assistance to manage the illness makes a significant contribution. The presence of certain internal (i.e. - sense of hope and connection) and external conditions (support of human rights and a culture of healing) are seen as more conducive to recovery (Jacobsen & Greenley, 2001). An increased sense of wellbeing irrespective of the presence of symptoms can also play a part in either reducing the symptoms or at least their severity (Davidson et al., 2006b).

The Self Righting Star® Framework (2012) was developed by Helen Glover to 'examine how recovery and self-righting processes apply' to 'support people to reclaim a life beyond the impact of illness, disability and adversity'. Glover considers self-righting to be a 'muscle of recovery' and describes a person's awareness of and ability to right or readjust at times of stress and destabilisation. While this mechanism is considered an intrinsic one, it can become compromised at times due to various factors, such as stressful incidents and environmental influences. At these times, input aimed at removing barriers and enhancing skills serves to strengthen a person's ability to 'get back up again' when they fall down. The Self Righting Star® consists of five arms, each representing a factor contributing to the experience of self-righting. While interconnected, these factors are separate and one does not necessarily lead to another or need to be addressed before or after another–they are non-linear in nature. Each arm has two polarities, which the individual constantly negotiates:

1. Active Sense of Hope -Hopelessness/ Despair
2. Ability to respond/take control-Inability to respond/take control
3. Active sense of self-Passive sense of self
4. Connectedness-Disconnection
5. Discovery-Alienation

Rather than focusing on a specific outcome, of greatest importance is the individual's ability to be aware of, hold and influence these polarities to achieve self-righting. The *how to* as well as the discovery elements of self-righting are far more instrumental to recovery than the outcome.

Self Righting Star® (diagram). (2012) copyright © Enlightened Consultants: used with permission

Sensory modulation can be considered an instrument for self-righting. At times when an individual 'tips over', or becomes dysregulated, sensory input can be utilised to stabilise the individual after they have experienced a period of instability. A better understanding of a person's unique sensory patterns and preferences will also reduce their vulnerability to becoming dysregulated as well as minimise barriers preventing the use of effective coping strategies to self-regulate. Active application of sensory modulation plays a significant role in a person's ability to move closer to the factors that positively contribute to the process of self-righting.

The concept of self-management was first documented in the 1960's in the context of the management of chronically ill children (Lorig & Holman, 2003) and then more widely adopted in the physical health arena (Wolf, 2011). It continued to be embraced by ever widening health circles, including mental health. Crepaz-Keay (2010) describes self-management as the ability to set goals and overcome the problems that are impediments in achieving these goals. Peer led programs have been shown to promote self-management and self-determination, thus building skills in self advocacy, increasing hope and supporting recovery (Cook et al, 2009). Self-management is in itself a tool to help a person take more control of their lives and lead a life worth living. It is therefore viewed as a 'close companion' to personal recovery (White, 2011). Sensory modulation assists people to develop and 0strengthen their self-management skills, and in doing so actively support recovery.

Self-regulation (particularly emotional regulation) and self-control can be considered one component of self-management. Glover's Self Righting Star® Framework (2012) incorporates the concepts of self-management and self-control. Sensory modulation supports a person to self-manage by using sensations to create a change in their emotional state. For example, splashing cold water on the face may help a person to feel less angry or anxious.

The formal acknowledgment of sensory modulation as a key component of recovery-informed practice within the various recovery frameworks and documents further strengthens its significance as a treatment modality across the mental health continuum of care. Individuals can actively acquire skills to self-manage illness symptoms and reduce stress. Using sensory modulation enhances occupational functioning and participation, which assists a person to work towards meaningful life goals and improve their quality of life.

Shepherd, Boardman, and Slade (2008) indicate that services promoting independence, self-management and self-mastery are adopting practices consistent with recovery principles. O'Hagan (2006) and Randal et al. (2009) stress that people who have developed patterns of destructive coping strategies to release or regain control (such as self-harm and aggression) are likely to persist unless supported to find effective alternatives. For individuals experiencing distress within psychiatric settings, the availability of a range of symptom management techniques is often limited. Interventions generally include clinician contact, medication, decreased stimulation or seclusion (Chalmers, Harrison, Mollison, Molloy, & Gray, 2012). A New Zealand study by Sutton and Nicholson (2011) found that utilising sensory modulation helped improve the person's ability to manage their own agitation and distress. When a person can calm themselves rather than relying on clinicians to calm them, they can then transfer these skills beyond the walls of the ward, into the home environment.

Actively engaging in opportunities to learn different ways to manage distress increases personal responsibility and growth, which are essential for recovery-oriented practice. An understanding of sensory modulation may help identify possible sensory explanations for impulsivity, aggression or risk-seeking behaviours, among others. Alternative strategies can then be developed to meet those sensory needs in a safe and appropriate manner (Dornan et al., 2009). Creating mindful distractions with the use of sensory modulation can divert attention away from distressing thoughts and destructive urges, and can be useful for people who are highly agitated. Bushman (2002) suggests that distraction is more helpful in reducing arousal than catharsis or the venting of pent-up aggression or anxiety.

It is important to note that individuals may already be using sensory modulation as a coping mechanism but may not realise they are doing so, or may not consider it a valid strategy. For example, swinging on a swing or wrapping up in a doona can be calming, while chewing gum or sucking on an icy drink can be grounding. By recognising its validity, individuals can incorporate these techniques into crisis or presentation plans. Documentation of strategies is essential, so they can be identified, referred to and reinforced by key stakeholders and support people when an individual is in crisis.

Sensory modulation and reducing restrictive practices

A significant driving force for mental health services to adopt sensory modulation is the need to develop 'alternative methods for managing distress, agitation and aggressive behaviour' (O'Hagan, 2006) to reduce seclusion and restraint practices.

In the United States in 2006, the National Association of State Mental Health Program Directors (NASMHPD) developed six core strategies to reduce seclusion and restraint. These strategies have been adopted by many other countries including Australia, New Zealand, the United Kingdom and a number of European countries. One of the core strategies recommends the use of 'de-escalation surveys or safety plans, use of person-first language, environmental changes to include comfort and sensory rooms; sensory modulation experiences and other meaningful treatment activities designed to teach people emotional self-management skills' (Huckshorn, 2006).

The use of sensory modulation has been shown to decrease the need for restraint and seclusion, and promote trauma-informed care (Champagne & Stromberg, 2004). Lloyd, King and Machingura (2014) found that the use of sensory approaches reduced levels of emotional disturbance as well as the frequency of seclusion episodes in an inpatient mental health environment. One study found that many participants who used a weighted blanket reported lowered anxiety levels and experienced measurably lowered electrodermal activity (Mullen, Champagne, Krishnamurthy, Dickson & Gao, 2008). Sutton and Nicholson (2011) found that the grounding and stabilising aspects of sensory modulation were a significant factor in de-escalation for clients who experienced psychosis, elevated mood, dissociation and overwhelming anxiety or who wanted to harm themselves. People using sensory modulation to calm themselves down are far less reliant on PRN medication or do not even require its use, or the use of seclusion or restraint, to manage emotional distress and dysregulation.

Despite policy directions strongly recommending the use of sensory modulation to reduce seclusion and restraint practices, some services struggle with implementation. This can stem from several reasons, including a lack of awareness of the evidence base behind sensory modulation, an uncertainty of how to apply the concepts and techniques to the environment, an inability to explain sensory modulation to others, and a lack of knowledge of how to adapt a clinical framework and service culture to effectively create service change. These reasons were a significant driving force for the development of this manual.

Before sensory modulation items are made available for use in different environments (such as inpatient units and waiting rooms), a risk/benefit analysis should be carried out to determine the suitability of these strategies in that environment. As well as highlighting any risks associated with using the techniques, the risk/benefit analysis should also consider the risks of NOT using them. For example, the availability of certain sensory items within a ward could result in some of the items being used in unintended ways, such as being thrown at someone. Conversely, not making such items accessible could result in increased risks associated with overuse or a reliance on heavily sedating PRN or antipsychotic medication, as well as the risk of not offering strategies to support a person to better learn to self-manage their symptoms and behaviours.

Sensory modulation and trauma-informed care

Most people with severe psychiatric disorders have experienced trauma, and the principles of trauma-informed care have been recommended as a universal mental health strategy (LeBel & Champagne, 2010). Trauma-informed care can be described as 'an organisational structure and treatment framework that involves understanding, recognising and responding to the effects of all types of trauma...(It) also emphasises physical, psychological and emotional safety for both consumers and providers, and helps survivors rebuild a sense of control and empowerment' (Trauma Informed Care Project, 2015).

In the process of working with and resolving trauma, Rothschild (2011) recommends paying attention and providing input into the sensory nervous system. Targeting treatment interventions at this level reinforces feelings of safety and security, which supports the development of increased control over symptoms. Cloitre and colleagues (2002) identify that the resolution of emotional dysregulation, dissociative symptoms and interpersonal problems is an important first step in treatment for people experiencing symptoms of complex post-traumatic stress disorder (PTSD). Research conducted by Kaiser, Gillette and Spinazzola (2010) found that sensory integration (SI) techniques combined with psychotherapy for the treatment of trauma resulted in symptom improvement in a number of domains.

Van Der Kolk (2006) also emphasised the importance of sensory input, specifically interoceptive (visceral) and body-oriented therapies for people with PTSD and trauma backgrounds. He recommended sensory modulation techniques including breathing and body movement, to support self-awareness and promote self-regulation. A study he conducted in 2014 (Van Der Kolk et al) demonstrated that a ten-week yoga program for women with PTSD significantly reduced participant PTSD symptoms: after the program concluded, some participants did not meet the criteria for PTSD. The study concluded that the sensory components of the yoga program, specifically physical (movement and proprioception) and interoceptive elements (breathing and awareness of bodily sensations) were critical variables in achieving these positive results.

An understanding of the components of the brain and how they affect the development of a sense of safety and security is helpful when supporting people with trauma backgrounds. The amygdale is a part of the limbic system involved in processing information from the senses. It plays an integral role in the ability to determine whether an environment is safe or dangerous. People who have experienced trauma have significant activity in their amygdala and therefore can perceive harmless environments and situations as very dangerous and unsafe. By using sensory modulation, a person can be supported to consider what helps to make an environment safe, including using sensory input that is calming and grounding, as well as the identification and management of potential aversive triggers. This intervention is also valuable when considering the sensations experienced in the body when feeling unsafe, and techniques to address or minimise these.

To illustrate, some people experience certain tactile input (such as fabrics or carpet) as aversive. Systematic exploration of each sense to identify potential triggers as well as sensations that are soothing can be beneficial. Experiential exploration can be useful for people who have not previously been consciously aware of their triggers. Ways of exploring sensory modulation in an experiential manner include presenting the person with a selection of items aimed at exploring the different senses, or accompanying the person into particular environments to observe how they respond/react. If the person says they hate or cannot stand a sensation, or refuses to explore it, this may indicate the presence of a noxious or aversive sensation particular to them. Such triggers may reflect their trauma history (e.g. the scent of the perpetrator); however certain triggers may also be due to a sensory sensitivity (e.g. the ringing of a bell) or a cognition (e.g. hating the music of Elvis). It is worthwhile identifying the existence of such triggers so they can be noted and incorporated into crisis management documents such as a personal safety plan.

Engaging in a process to develop a plan for managing potential sensory triggers can also have the benefit of changing the individual's relationship with their body as they identify that there are some safe or soothing sensations (Koomar, Warner & Westcott, 2009). These soothing sensations can then become useful for self-management of emotions, dissociation or body sensations (Linehan, 2015).

Sensory modulation strategies are most useful for crisis intervention when they are personalised. A sensation that calms one person can be a trigger for another; thus, the emphasis needs to be on providing options for clients to choose sensory modulation strategies themselves or to have developed a list of sensory modulation strategies prior to a crisis. Potential sensory modulation strategies that could be useful for clients include blankets, wraps, ice packs, ear plugs, music, rocking or massage chairs (Champagne, 2011; Sutton & Nicholson, 2011). In an inpatient mental health unit, these strategies may be documented in a personal safety plan and available for the person to use.

For all individuals, sensory modulation is most clinically effective when used as a trauma-informed recovery initiative. This way, it is used within a framework that is also person centred, individualised and recovery based. Without the alignment of these core principles, like any technique it has the potential to become misused and an intervention that could be traumatising, controlling and disempowering for clients. For example, if not used correctly, a sensory room can become a space associated with concepts of behavioural control, punishment and reward.

Dialectical behaviour therapy and sensory modulation

Clinicians who are familiar with dialectical behaviour therapy (DBT) would already be using some sensory modulation strategies (although this term is not used in DBT). These include using the dive reflex or engaging in intense exercise (TIP skill), self-soothing through the five senses and engaging in distracting activities to survive a difficult moment. (Linehan 2015, Miller et al 2012). Some of these strategies use cognitive distraction while others change the physiology of an emotion. Sensory modulation employs eight senses to provide a wider range of sensations than DBT. It also adopts a different theoretical base, which involves using:

- movement including swinging and rocking (e.g. to calm)
- deep pressure strategies including weighted items
- proprioceptive strategies including pulling and pushing muscles and heavy work
- interoception including bowel, bladder, thirst, hunger (not only breathing and heartrate)
- vestibular input including spinning (for example to provide exhilaration or numbing)
- vibration and temperature changes as further tactile sensations
- sensory modulation to stay alert (such as listening to a lecture or driving a car)
- emphasis on power sensations
- the sense of smell which is linked to memory, safety and attachment
- an occupational therapy theoretical base regarding sensory processing, including an understanding of individual differences regarding processing sensory input and tailoring strategies to the individual.

It is also important to note that sensory modulation is not seen as purely a cognitive distraction, so the intensity and choice of the sensations are relevant considerations

Who does sensory modulation work for?

The short answer to this is that **everyone** can positively benefit from sensory modulation. If faced with a situation where we want to change our feelings, alter our mood, improve our sense of self and enhance our functioning, engaging in sensory modulation can help achieve this. Many people use sensory modulation on a daily basis without consciously thinking about it. Using a scented bath gel in the shower and eating crunchy cereal to wake up in the morning, and going for a walk or a swim after work to calm down are all examples of applying sensory modulation in everyday life.

When a person experiences illness, stress, injury or disability, they often engage in fewer meaningful life experiences or roles. The consequences of this can often include feeling less connected to or less engaged in the activities that provide the sensory stimulation that contributes to health and wellbeing. Sensory modulation can therefore provide the person with much needed sensory input so they can move closer to their optimum sensory levels, improve resilience and enhance their ability to cope with their current health issues.

How sensory modulation can help

Sensory modulation can be very helpful when a person is:

- agitated and highly distressed (anger, dementia-related agitation and distress)
- feeling overwhelmed
- unable to respond or feeling frozen
- feeling lethargic or having low energy
- having difficulty with concentration and focus
- experiencing extremely intense emotions (sadness, shame, disappointment)
- experiencing mood symptoms (depression, anxiety, panic)
- feeling detached, unreal, disconnected or dissociated
- feeling hopeless and helpless (in a crisis)
- experiencing hallucinations
- experiencing pain.

What does sensory modulation do?

Sensory modulation can change how a person feels in a number of ways, including:

- calming and grounding
- helping to focus or wake up
- improving mindfulness
- providing an alternative to self-harm or addictive substances
- increasing feelings of pleasure or thrill
- distracting from or controlling urges
- connecting to a friend or loved one
- coping with illness, injury, symptoms and pain.

When to use sensory modulation

Sensory modulation can be used:

- as part of the rhythm and routine of everyday life
- as an introduction or orientation to a facility or service, where individuals can be educated about sensory modulation and availability of use
- in a crisis in the community
- in an inpatient or care unit, when a person is becoming emotionally dysregulated (when distressed by symptoms, agitated by self-care tasks, experiencing an upsetting interaction with a family member or co-patient, or about to see a doctor)
- to augment and support activity engagement (participating in an appointment, catching the bus, coping with a dental appointment or medical procedure)
- to help promote feelings of safety and security (for individuals with a trauma background, or to help feel grounded and safe).

Where to use sensory modulation

Sensory modulation can be used in:

- inpatient units (including mental health and physical health, and in dementia wards)
- outpatient clinics, rehabilitation and community care units
- emergency centres
- community centres
- GP clinics, medical centres
- counselling and therapy centres
- the home environment
- welfare services and homeless shelters
- dental clinics
- schools (chill-out zones in classrooms or on campus, or in a counsellor waiting room)
- any situation in the community to manage distress and improve functioning (using public transport, in a shopping centre, while in self-care activities, participating in a group program, clinical interview or appointment).

Chapter 3:

The Eight Senses

The Eight Senses

To sense is to be able to 'pick up' or perceive information originating from the environment or internally from our own bodies. The perception and experience of this information is gained through our senses. The sensory system is the part of the central nervous system responsible for collecting and processing information received through the senses of sight, sound, touch, taste, smell, movement, proprioception and interoception.

Sensory input is most often 'multimodal', meaning information is received from a number of sensory systems at once. For example, when walking on the beach, we pick up a combination of sight, sound, touch, smell and movement sensory input. The sensory system influences our perception of and response to sensory input. With this in mind, the sensory system plays an integral role in our ability to:

- register and interpret information obtained from the environment and obtained internally (visceral sensations)
- make sense of the world around us, recognise and respond to danger and decide how to proceed (for example, with caution, enthusiasm or ease)
- keep safe
- feel calm, relaxed, focused or alert
- feel connected to ourselves, the world and other people
- understand our own likes, dislikes, patterns and preferences
- bring pleasure, enjoyment and fun to our lives, and add 'colour'.

The sensory system is connected to and affects our arousal and stress levels. Consequentially, it is an essential link to understanding ourselves and the environment around us, and to support our ability to function effectively in the environment.

The eight different sensory systems

- movement/vestibular
- touch
- taste and oral motor movement
- sight
- sound/auditory
- smell/olfaction
- interoception.

The following exploration of each sensory system will incorporate:

- information on each sense
- examples of sensitive responses to sensory input
- examples of seeking responses to sensory input
- suggestions for using the sense for sensory modulation.

Movement/vestibular

Movement provides information relating to the body and takes into account gravity, speed, size and head position. The vestibular system is critical in the sensation of movement. It comprises small bones in the inner ears, which are bathed in a special fluid. In detecting head movement, the changes in the direction of the fluid are detected by microscopic hairs (sensory receptors) located on the bones. This provides feedback on all movements and is involved in the planning of future movement. Examples of the movement/vestibular system in action include:

- knowing the position of the body and when the body is lying down or sitting up
- the feeling of moving when in an elevator or car
- being able to walk along uneven terrain
- being able to run fast until the finish line in a race.

The movement/vestibular system has a role in the development and maintenance of muscle tone, posture, balance, equilibrium and coordination. It is involved in the coordination of eye and head movements, and is essential in performing tasks such as looking to and from a point in the distance, reading across a page, scanning the environment and tracking a moving object in space. It also plays a role in the development of some aspects of language. Movement sensations stem from a variety of activities incorporating different types of movement (walking, running, swimming, cycling), the pace of movement (fast versus slow, gentle, regular) and the direction of movement (forward, backward, up and down, tumbling, spinning).

Deep touch, proprioceptive and movement sensory input often occurs in combination. There are many daily activities that increase this sensory input, for example, outdoor activities such as gardening and watering, domestic activities such as cleaning the shower, cooking and sweeping, leisure activities such as swimming, walking and dancing, and creative activities such as working with clay, drawing, and playing a musical instrument.

A person who is more sensitive to movement/vestibular input may:

- get motion sickness more often than others
- find travelling in lifts and on escalators unsettling
- dislike the feeling of fast swinging, hanging upside down and theme park rides
- find it harder to maintain balance compared to other people.

A person who is less sensitive or seeks movement/vestibular input may:

- enjoy participating in high energy and/or adventure activities
- seem to move around a lot, find it hard to keep still, and walk quickly
- like travelling in cars, on boats or motorbikes, or cycling.

Using movement/vestibular input in sensory modulation

Vestibular input is one of the three power sensations (the other two being proprioception and touch). This means it can be considered one of the strongest options for calming and regulating emotions, and to help a person feel more grounded and safe. Some examples are:

- practising tai chi, yoga, or stretching to feel calm and reduce stress
- going for a walk, swinging in a hammock or rocking to feel grounded

- swimming, jogging, bouncing a ball, and dancing to music to feel more energised and connected
- running on the spot or skipping rope to reduce agitation
- reducing the intensity, variability or speed of movement if movement sensitive.

Proprioception

Proprioception is the awareness of our body in space, or the ability to know the position of our body and limbs without visual input. The position-sense sensory receptors are located in the muscles and tendons. When we move, we push and pull against the muscles and create resistance, which triggers these receptors.

Proprioception has an important role in the planning, organising and carrying out of movement by helping people judge distances (so as not to bump into things) and in determining the physical effort needed for a particular movement (for example, throwing a ball a specific distance, picking up a delicate object, or applying pressure to write).

Because it provides information on where we are in the environment, many people find that proprioception helps them to feel more grounded, organised, settled and centred.

Ways to increase proprioceptive input include:

- heavy work such as gardening, carrying buckets of water and scrubbing the bath
- deep pressure such as placing a heavy item on the body (a pet or bag of rice), wearing a weighted shoulder wrap or using a weighted exercise vest
- wearing tight clothing such as skins or tight leggings, or sleeping in a sleeping bag
- exercise that involves pushing or pulling the muscles of the body
- eating crunchy or chewy food, providing oral motor sensory input to the mouth.

People who seek out proprioceptive input may:

- enjoy sports and activities that involve crashing or jumping, such as trampolining or rugby, or they may be children who enjoy running and crashing into mummy's legs
- feel calm under many heavy blankets or towels
- wear tight, heavy or layered clothing such as skins, thermals, heavy jackets and stockings
- chew pens and other items, or enjoy chewy and crunchy food.

People who are more sensitive to proprioceptive input may:

- react negatively to having something heavy placed on their lap
- sleep better without a doona or blanket
- dislike many types of exercise or tight or heavy clothing.

People who don't notice proprioceptive input may:

- be unaware of their posture or body positioning and walk into doorways
- drop items because they don't grip them tightly enough.

Using proprioceptive input in sensory modulation

Proprioceptive input is one of the three power sensations (the other two power sensations being vestibular and touch). This means it can be considered one of the strongest options for calming and regulating emotions, and to help a person feel more grounded and safe. Some examples include:

- placing heavy items on a person's lap or around their shoulders
- engaging in activities that involve pushing or pulling, such as gardening, sweeping, or pushing a pram
- pulling a shawl or towel tightly around a person's shoulders
- practising more exercise (resistance or stretching and activities such as yoga).

Touch

Touch receptors are located in the skin, some close to the surface (around the hair follicles) and others deeper, near the muscles and tendons. Touch is important for safety, understanding, communication, and can increase feelings of connection to ourselves and others.

There are different types of touch receptors:

1. Light touch

Light touch is the feeling of a feather stroking an arm, a breeze on the face, or loose clothing in contact with the skin. It tends to send the brain a message to 'pay attention', increasing alertness and awareness of what is going on. However, some people may find a certain light touch quite soothing, such as having their hair brushed or a gentle stroke on their back. Touch that originates from a trusted person, and touch that the person is able to control tends to be more calming.

2. Deep touch/pressure

Deep pressure is the feeling of a deep massage, wearing firm clothing such as jeans or a heavy jumper, being wrapped in a blanket or receiving a big hug. Deep touch tends to illicit a comforting, grounding feeling.

3. Temperature

Skin temperature includes feeling warm or cold, or feeling changes in temperature.

4. Pain receptors

Pain receptors provide information about pain and itch and can originate from tissue damage, extreme temperature and noxious chemicals.

5. Vibration

These receptors provide information about vibration (movement on the skin) and texture. Texture is sensed when the skin touches a surface, causing little vibrations as the skin moves across the surface.

A person who is more sensitive to touch may:

- dislike the feeling of tags in clothing or particular textures on their skin

- find extreme changes in temperature uncomfortable, such as cold air-conditioning
- avoid getting their hands dirty
- prefer to stand a distance away from others in queues.

A person who is less sensitive to touch or who prefers touch input may:

- enjoy the feeling of getting massages, their hair cut, and the breeze on their face
- frequently walk barefoot
- not be bothered by mess on their hands such as garden soil, or food during meal preparation
- be touchy and feely, and fiddle with things a lot.

Using touch in sensory modulation

Touch input is one of the three power sensations (the other two being proprioception and vestibular input). This means it can be considered one of the strongest options for calming and regulating emotions, and to help a person feel more grounded and safe. Some examples include:

- wearing a heavy shawl or towel that is wrapped around their shoulders, or placing a doona over their body when feeling anxious
- sitting with books, a heavy bag, a bag of rice, or a pet dog on their lap to feel grounded
- lifting weights, bags or buckets of water to feel calm
- receiving a firm handshake or a hug, or getting a massage to self-soothe
- fidgeting with an item to manage stress
- reducing unnecessary touch input (cutting tags off clothes or wearing gardening gloves).

Taste and oral motor movement

The sensation of taste incorporates five different taste receptors of sweet, salty, sour, bitter and umami (savoury/meat). The taste buds act as the receptors and are located on the top surface of the tongue. Like the sense of smell, taste is triggered by a chemical reaction. Flavour is the combination of taste and smell.

While the sense of taste is very strong at birth, several factors can diminish taste over time, including aging, the use of cigarettes, alcohol and other drugs, pollution, certain viruses and bacteria.

Other important sensory considerations related to taste are texture (hard, soft, crunchy, chewy, thick, runny) and oral motor movement. Oral motor sensory input comes from the movement and contraction of muscles in the face and jaw when we use our mouths, as in the following:

- sucking (through a straw or on a lollypop)
- licking (ice, ice cream or fruit)
- sipping (a hot or cold drink)
- chewing (gum, ice, raw fruit or vegetables, popcorn).

There are several non-eating related oral movements, which can also provide oral motor sensory input, such as:

- whistling and singing
- humming and blowing bubbles or balloons
- tongue clicking.

A person who prefers strong taste and a high level of oral motor input may:

- like intense flavours such as spice and chilli, and add salt and sugar to foods
- enjoy a variety of different tastes and textures
- put things in or to their mouth a lot (such as chewing gum, pens or their nails)
- whistle, hum, click their tongue or smack their lips together.

A person who is more sensitive to taste and oral motor sensory input may:

- avoid strongly flavoured foods and stick to the same known tastes and food choices
- dislike particular food textures (such as peanut butter or the furry skin of fruit)
- dislike the feeling of cleaning their teeth
- gag easily or have difficulty swallowing tablets.

Using taste and oral motor sensory input in sensory modulation

Some examples are:

- adding preferred tastes and flavours to meals to increase enjoyment
- using citrus, mint and spicy flavours to increase feelings of energy
- chewing gum or crunchy food to improve focus
- sucking on a cold slushy drink through a straw to help feel grounded
- eating pumpkin soup using grandma's recipe to remind us of her and to feel nurtured.

Sight

Sight or vision is the ability of the eyes to receive images created by visible light, which are converted to electrical nerve impulses and transmitted to the brain. Visual perception is the ability of the brain to process and interpret these impulses. In doing so, the brain distinguishes the following various factors:

- colour and shape
- size and brightness (light versus dark)
- movement.

The brain also has the ability to recognise, differentiate and interpret visual stimuli by comparing such stimuli with visual experiences made earlier in life. For example, the brain can determine whether a particular visual image is bigger than, smaller than, brighter, shinier, or less hairy than a previously observed image.

A person who is less sensitive to or seeks visual input may:

- enjoy bright colours and contrasts in the environment
- like windows and doors open to let light in and view scenery
- prefer a variety of visual scenes and environments
- be very good at visual puzzles and games or spotting discrepancies

- enjoy fast-moving racing cars or bird watching.

A person who is more sensitive to visual sensory input may:

- find artificial light too bright or harsh and prefer dimmer light
- prefer muted tones and uncluttered, minimalist environments
- have difficulty finding objects in a busy environment
- draw the curtains at home to block out visual stimuli
- find that fast-moving visual images provoke anxiety, for example, moths or crowds.

Using visual sensory input for sensory modulation

Some examples include:

- altering the brightness of the environment to suit sensory preferences
- hanging up photos or pictures of landscapes (beach, rainforest or mountains)
- collecting items in favourite colours for the home (throw rug, cushion, or choosing a certain colour for a room)
- reducing clutter in the house and keeping spaces simple and tidy
- using an umbrella or wearing a hat in public to reduce the amount of visual processing
- reducing light/glare by using sunglasses, tinted glasses or reducing the brightness of computer screens.

Sound/auditory

Sound is experienced by the ears detecting vibration, which is caused by pressure changes in our surroundings. As with sight, the auditory system relies on how the brain interprets, recognises and differentiates the sensory stimuli.

The auditory system can differentiate between different sounds, intensities and locations. Also, an important connection exists between memory and sound (for example, being able to memorise multiple numbers and number patterns, such as a phone number, and remembering familiar sounds).

From a sensory perspective, different sounds can have an activating effect, while others can be calming (Dunn, 2009).

Calming sounds tend to have the following characteristics:

- soft and slow
- rhythmic and simple
- predictable and familiar.

Activating sounds tend to have the following characteristics:

- strong/pronounced and fast paced
- non-rhythmic and complex
- unpredictable.

A person who is less sensitive to or likes more noise may:

- turn up the volume of the television or radio

- not be bothered by or tend not to notice loud noises in the environment
- struggle to hear their name when called in crowds
- make a lot of noise themselves (tapping, whistling, singing or humming).

A person who is more sensitive to noise may:

- look uncomfortable or place their hands over their ears when noises are too loud for them
- find difficulty concentrating when there is more noise in the environment
- feel bothered by household noise and ask for the TV or radio to be turned down
- close doors or shush people when they are talking on the phone.

Using sound sensory input for sensory modulation

Some examples are:

- waking up in the morning to upbeat music and unwinding with classical melodies
- using ear plugs or headphones to tone down loud noises
- listening to sounds of nature to increase feelings of calm
- singing along to songs when feeling uptight
- listening to music with a strong beat (e.g. gangster rap) to help feel grounded.

Smell/olfaction

Smell is the ability to perceive scent, which is the presence of odour molecules in the air, detected by hundreds of olfactory receptors in the nostrils. Scent receptors are excited to different degrees and it is this variable combination of excitement processed by the brain that creates smell. The chemical nature of smell seems particularly important in the reception and coding process that occurs in the brain.

The sense of smell enhances our environmental awareness and is especially important to alert us of potential environmental dangers, such as fire, a gas leak or rancid food. Certain smells (for example, a freshly mowed lawn, baking cookies or a sea breeze) can significantly influence how we feel.

Smell is closely connected to the limbic system, which is involved in memory and emotions. Therefore, many people find that certain smells can be powerful triggers for memories and emotions, which can be a pleasant or unpleasant experience depending on the trigger and its meaning to the individual. It is important to have a prearranged plan to implement in case strong memories and emotions are evoked through sensory exploration. This could include using movement, stretching, talking to a trusted person, or engaging in an alternative sensory activity that increases feelings of calm and safety.

A person who is less sensitive to or likes more intense smells may:

- be drawn towards intense-smelling items (soaps, perfumes, herbs, flowers or incense)
- need higher amounts or a higher intensity of smell to be able to notice a smell
- enjoy a larger variety of different smells
- be able to tolerate complex or several layers of smells occurring at the same time.

A person who is more sensitive to smell may:

- notice aromas or smells in the environment faster than others
- quickly notice and find certain smells unpleasant (cooking, petrol, cleaning products or perfumes)
- avoid perfume counters in department stores
- be good at noticing the subtle differences between smells.

Using smell input for sensory modulation

Some examples are:

- placing herbs or favourite scented plants in the garden or on a window ledge
- diffusing preferred essential oils in warm water (lavender, eucalyptus or sandalwood)
- using citrus body wash in the morning to help wake up
- smelling a favourite food while cooking it, to self-soothe
- identifying the scent of a safe person (clothing or aftershave) to remind us we have safe people in our lives.

Interoception

Interoception is a lesser known sensory system sometimes referred to as the visceral (internal organ) sense. It detects internal regulation responses in our internal organs. It is believed that in helping to make sense of our internal state, interoceptive sensory input plays a role in influencing our mood, emotions and sense of wellbeing (Cameron, 2002). The insula is thought to play an important role in the emotional processing of this sensation, due to its function of connecting interoceptive awareness with affective experience (Wiebking & Northoff, 2014).

Interoceptive sensations include breathing, hunger, thirst, heart rate, internal body temperature, stomach pain or discomfort, and the feeling of a headache, the urge to vomit, and the urge to empty the bladder or bowel and sexual urges.

Interoceptive awareness can assist in the maintenance of optimal internal stability and regulation, which can promote a more stable sense of self and feelings of physical and emotional security. Research by Shulz and Vogele (2015) and Dunn et al. (2010) shows a connection between interoceptive experience and mental health, in that people with depression tend to exhibit lower registration of visceral cues, whereas people with anxiety tend to have heightened awareness of visceral cues.

If a person is less aware of interceptive information they may:

- notice feelings of stress and anxiety later than others
- not address important physiological needs in a timely manner, such as eating and drinking
- miss early cues to empty bowels or bladder, only noticing when sensations are very strong
- be unaware that they are overheating or too cold
- be prone to overeating because they are less able to recognise signs of fullness
- be less sensitive to markers of ill health (aches and pains, headaches, chills) and may not seek health interventions soon enough
- have difficulty identifying the sensations of emotions in their body.

If a person is very sensitive to interoceptive information (visceral cues) they may:

- feel bombarded and overwhelmed by internal information, such as a churning stomach, pounding heart or dry throat
- find it hard to focus on or prioritise external environmental input
- have difficulty concentrating and are prone to distraction if physiological needs are not met
- pick up on internal cues very quickly, which can be distracting and interfere with activities
- be misinterpreted and labelled as being hyperchondriacal or emotionally impulsive.

Using awareness of interoception for sensory modulation

Some examples are:

- establishing and maintaining basic self-care so that it is part of the daily routine (eating, drinking, resting, relaxing, seeing the doctor)
- clarifying information with others (temperature, outward signs of stress)
- making sure that self-care needs are addressed in a timely fashion
- having a range of effective and easy-to-access strategies to manage stress and anxiety.

Chapter 4:

How Sensory Modulation Works

Changing how you feel

To understand how using sensory modulation changes how we feel, it is helpful to look at what is meant by 'how you feel'. This phrase can refer to the experience of the physiology of the body (for example, to feel sick, hungry, in pain, cold or tense) Or it can refer to the alertness and focus of the brain (for example, awake, unfocused or tired). 'How you feel' can also describe experiencing emotions such as feeling sad, happy, angry or scared. When sensory modulation is described as an intervention that can change the way you feel, it is describing the possible shifting of any of these described states, through using sensory input.

As a therapeutic intervention, sensory modulation is most commonly used to change strong emotions, manage pain or to improve focus.

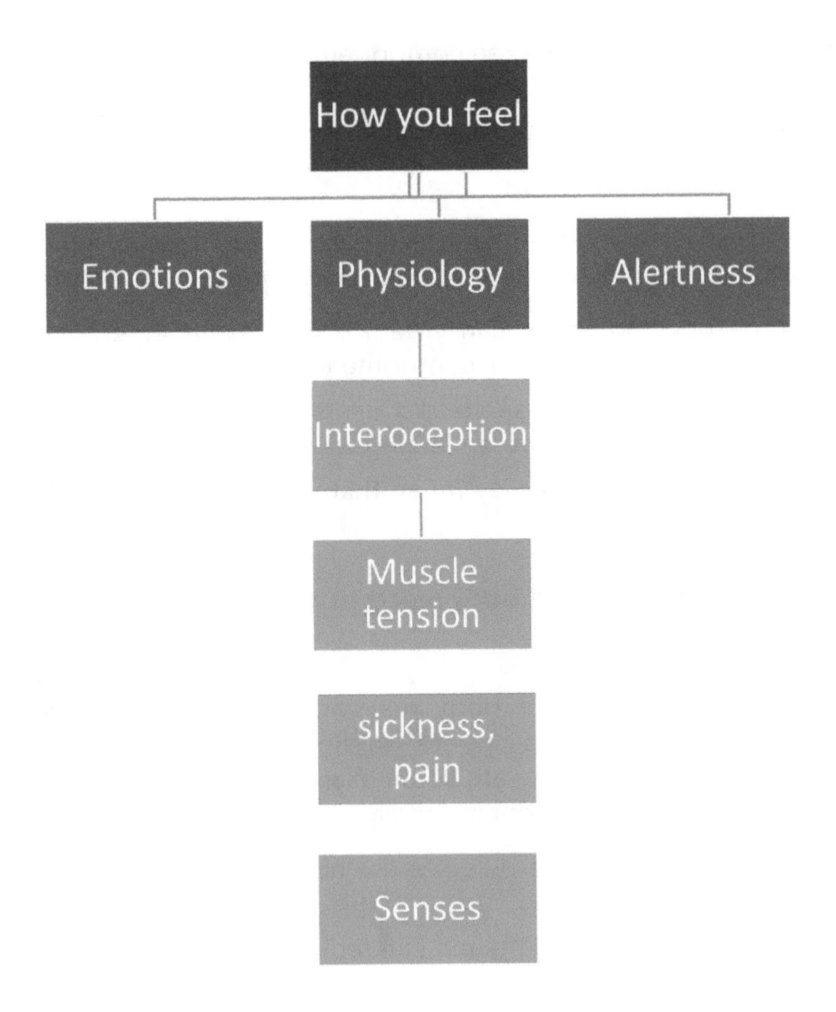

How you feel (diagram) (2017) copyright © Fitzgibbon and O'Sullivan.

Changing emotions

Emotions tend to last for seconds, minutes or hours, while a mood labels an emotion that is felt for a longer duration–sometimes days or weeks. A diagnosis of mental illness, anxiety or depression means that the person experiences an array of symptoms including a change in mood, which affects their day-to-day functioning for an extended period.

Emotions have three components:

1. **a subjective experience**–how we think about an event, for example, 'that driver braking suddenly makes me angry'
2. **a physiological response**–how our body reacts to an event internally, for example, an increased blood flow to the hands and face, an increased heart rate or adrenaline pumping around the body
3. **a behavioural or expressive response**–what we do, for example, 'I am going to yell at that driver' (Hockenbury & Hockenbury, 2007).

Sensory modulation can work on all three components of emotions, as described below:

1. A subjective experience–how we think about an event

Change our thinking

Sensory modulation can change our thinking by creating a new sensory event that stimulates new thoughts. This can then create a new emotion. Here are some examples:

- playing some uplifting music can create a new event or emotion. If a song is perceived as really good, this will contribute to feeling happy
- smelling mum's perfume can serve as a reminder that we are loved by somebody and help us to feel love rather than feeling worthless and unlovable
- doing something distracting may mean that we are not thinking about the event that caused the emotion.

2. A physiological response–how our body reacts to an event internally

Change or reduce the physiology

Sensory modulation can change our body reactions or physiological responses. Such changes can occur by reversing the current physiological response or by providing a different physiological response. Here are some examples of sensory modulation used to change how our body reacts to an event internally:

- splashing icy water on the face reverses the hot flushed feeling experienced when angry
- smelling a scent can be grounding and can reduce dissociation
- rocking in a rocking chair can calm an agitated person with dementia.

3. A behavioural or expressive response–what we do

Change the usual behavioural or expressive response to a different response

Sensory modulation can provide an alternative to engaging in a behavioural or expressive response. Often, the behavioural response to an emotion contributes to a maladaptive or destructive outcome, such as self-harm, aggression, smoking, or substance use.

The brain links our thinking, physiology and behaviours together. A change in one of these, even just once, can lead to a change in emotions. Regular practice of sensory modulation at the time the emotion commences assists to changing the physiology and behavioural expression, which lays the foundation for the development of new habits. The brain's ability to discard old habits and learn new ones requires growing new neurones in a process known as neurogenesis.

Examples of using sensory modulation to change a learnt behaviour or expressive response into another response includes:

- using a weighted cushion instead of punching a wall
- applying a cold spray on the arm instead of self-harming
- rocking in a hammock rather than eating comfort food.

Alerting

Alerting sensations can lead to us feeling more awake and being able to focus and concentrate. These are particularly useful for people feeling drowsy, sedated or having difficulty focusing on a task at hand such as concentrating on someone talking or reading. For some people, a repetitive sound or visual image can make them feel drowsy. This could include listening to a lecturer with a monotone voice or driving along a highway. Some people get used to sensory input very quickly (known as habituation) and therefore may benefit from adding more or creating a variety of sensory input, as strong and variable sensations are generally the most alerting. To illustrate this point, think about getting a little drowsy when driving. What strategies could you use to help? Common strategies include winding down the window to allow cool air to enter, turning up the music, chewing a mint or scanning the road for interesting cars. Relying on thinking alone to wake up would not be likely to work as quickly and effectively as increasing the sensory input.

Eating

Eating chewy, crunchy or strongly flavoured food can be alerting. This stimulates our facial muscles and our sensory motor cortex (Hirano et al., 2015).

Visual Input

Looking at bright, coloured, flashing or a variety of visual images can be alerting.

Blue light is found on a lot of technology screens such as smart phones, tablets and computer monitors. This blue light has been found to be alerting as it activates the 'wake up' part of the brain called the reticular activating system.

Creating resistance

By pushing our feet into the floor, pushing our hands together, walking or jumping, we can stimulate the deep touch receptors in our body that provide awareness of our body in space (proprioception). Creating more sensations in our body increases bodily awareness and a feeling of connection to the present moment.

Being aware of alerting sensations is important when we are trying to calm down or get to sleep! Sensory modulation techniques may include turning off blue light (personal technology such as computers, laptops, smart phones and tablets) at least half an hour before going to bed, and trying to mask sudden sounds (e.g. playing white noise to tune out outside noises). Exposure to natural light during the day has been shown to reduce the effect of blue light on arousal levels.

Grounding sensations

Grounding is a term referring to the feeling of awareness and connection to our body and environment. Grounding is a useful coping strategy when feeling spacey or numb, or experiencing flashbacks, dissociation or high levels of anxiety. It works by increasing sensory input so that the sensations of our body within the environment are more noticeable. The following list details some ways to provide grounding input:

- **creating resistance:** by pushing our feet into the floor, pushing our hands together, walking or jumping, we can stimulate the deep touch receptors in our body that provide awareness of our body in space (proprioception). Providing increased levels of sensation for the body assists to increase bodily awareness and connection to the present moment.
- **deep pressure:** by putting books, a heavy handbag, or a dog on our lap, we can stimulate the deep touch receptors to increase bodily awareness and connection to self and the moment.
- **using scents:** by increasing smell input such as by smelling the perfume of a loved one, we can activate an immediate pathway to the limbic system. Smell is the only sense that does not travel through the brainstem first, and it has a strong and fast connection to positive or negative memories.
- **movement:** by rocking, jumping on the spot or walking, we can stimulate the vestibular, proprioception and touch receptors. This increases their input to the cerebellum, which in turn regulates the autonomic nervous system.

Intense sensations

In dialectical behaviour therapy, or DBT (Lineman, 2015), intense sensations are recommended when a client is feeling an urge to self-harm, to use drugs or alcohol or to engage in ineffective coping behaviours. Most intense sensations are also grounding. A significant difference between intense and soothing sensations is that intense sensations are often not experiences that are pleasant or nurturing. However, the objective of using intense sensations is to increase a strong sensory input to reconnect with the body and promote a feeling of grounding.

An example of an intense sensation is the use of icy water to decrease the heart rate. The icy water can be either applied from a bowl or applied to the area under the eyes in a zip lock bag filled with water. The breath is then held. The combination of holding our breath and applying icy water activates the mammalian dive reflex. This reflex has the biological function of decreasing our heart rate to preserve the body and brain if a person falls into icy water. By decreasing the heart rate and increasing carbon dioxide levels in the blood (by holding our breath), our feelings of calm and grounding increase. Note that this technique should not be used by people who have a heart problem or other medical problems where it would be contraindicated to drop the heart rate quickly, such as anorexia nervosa.

Other examples of intense sensations include warhead lollies or chilli, loud music, strong scents, or swinging on a swing.

Managing pain, discomfort and itch

Sensory modulation strategies that may be useful for managing pain and itch include deep pressure touch, vibration and changed temperature. These may work by providing an alternative sensory input to the pain or itch receptors. This theory is known as the *gate control* theory of pain and it proposes that the pain signals are inhibited by the competing sensory information (Melzack & Wall, 1965). This has significant positive implications for supporting the management of several conditions involving pain, itch and discomfort, including the following:

- skin conditions such as burns, psoriasis and dermatitis
- gut conditions causing discomfort
- chronic pain conditions
- chronic fatigue conditions
- vestibular dysfunction such as dizziness and migraines.

Soothing

Soothing is a term that refers to feeling nurtured and reassured. We can soothe other people or ourselves.

Self-soothing is useful when feeling self-hatred or shame, sadness or anxiety. Some therapeutic frameworks, for example, DBT (Lineman, 2015), emphasise the intention to self- nurture in addition to the action of self-soothing. Although we sometimes feel very undeserving of nurturing, soothing actions can still soothe the body, which in turn can help soothe the mind.

The strongest soothing sensations are those that involve the large muscles of the body. These include rocking and other large, slow movements, deep pressure and touch.

To further explore the concept and strategies of self-soothing, we can think about the ways in which we soothe a baby. This can include rocking, holding the baby firmly, rhythmical patting, singing or talking, giving the baby something to suck, or something to smell that reminds the baby of an attachment figure. Using these strategies as adolescents or adults may remind us of how we were soothed as a baby. New soothing experiences can also be beneficial.

Infant soothing translated to adolescents and adults

Rocking

- **baby:** in a rocking chair, in one's arms, in a baby rocker, in the car
- **adolescent or adult:** in a swing chair, in a rocking chair, in a hammock
- **why it works:** the rhythmic movement stimulates the vestibular receptors and autonomic nervous system.

Firm hug, wrapping

- **baby:** firmly hugging the baby, wrapping the baby in blanket
- **adolescent or adult:** placing a handbag or a dog on one's lap, getting under a heavy doona, wearing tight clothes, receiving a firm hug

- **why it works:** the firm pressure provides awareness of body position in space (proprioception) and stimulates the autonomic nervous system. When being hugged, there is also the benefit of feeling cared for by another person.

Rhythmic touch

- **baby:** patting
- **adolescent or adult:** drumming, dancing
- **why it works:** the rhythmic movement, sound and touch stimulates the vestibular, auditory and touch receptors and autonomic nervous system. The heartbeat and breathing becomes 'entrained' to the rhythm (Trost, Labbe & Grandjean, 2017).

Sucking

- **baby:** sucking, eating
- **adolescent or adult:** sucking, eating, singing
- **why it works:** sucking stimulates the facial muscles that regulate the limbic system (Fosha, Siegel, & Solomon, 2009), eating can send a message to the autonomic nervous system that it is time to 'rest and digest', and sucking strongly and chewing can provide proprioceptive input to the mouth.

Sound

- **baby:** lullaby, parent's voice, music, familiar sounds
- **adolescent or adult:** music, a loved one's voice, familiar sounds
- **why it works:** a familiar voice or familiar sounds provide a sense of safety, with the heartbeat and breathing becoming 'entrained' to the rhythm–music stimulates the auditory receptors and autonomic nervous system.

Scent

- **baby:** a parent's scent, which can be applied to a cloth
- **adolescent or adult:** partner's deodorant, mum's t-shirt, grandma's soap, perfume
- **why it works:** olfactory input follows a very quick pathway to the brain and is strongly linked with memory. A reminder of a loved one may help us to feel safe.

Relaxation and calming

Relaxation refers to the mind and body being at ease. The body is free from muscle tension and the mind is free from negative emotions including anxiety and irritation.

Common relaxation techniques include the following

- progressive muscle relaxation
- breathing exercises
- visualisation
- mental distraction.

In the field of psychology, relaxation exercises have traditionally included guided imagery, autonomic breathing and progressive muscle relaxation. Each of these techniques has a strong cognitive component, with benefits likely to be achieved through mental focus: for example, using the mind to slow down breathing, or to create a visual distraction. In addition, by focusing on something else, a person does not think about the things that are upsetting them. Completing these exercises can be very effective methods to change one's mood. Learning and practising strategies such as mindfulness can increase the ability to focus and achieve a relaxed state. These relaxation exercises can be described as top down processes, in that the thinking part of the brain is driving the relaxation process.

However, many people have difficulties using relaxation exercises with a strong cognitive component when experiencing intense emotions such as anger, shame or panic. Sensory modulation offers another option by using the senses rather than cognitions to change the mood. The calming benefit achieved can be described as a bottom up process, in that sensory input is received through the body and travels up the brainstem to the brain to directly alter physiological arousal levels. For this reason, the term 'calming' rather than 'relaxing' is used, as it better reflects the action mechanism of sensory input to the body, and not just from a process of distracting the mind, which is more of a cognitive process.

Calming sensations can calm down or reduce the physiological arousal that occurs with strong emotions. There are individual differences in how we experience the sensation of calm. For some people, the sensation of calm is achieved through a relaxed mind and body. However, for others, the feeling of letting go of muscle tension can increase feelings of vulnerability. The dislike of letting go of muscular tension can be something experienced by people with a trauma history (Rothschild, 2010).

In these circumstances, a retained feeling of muscular tension may contribute to an increased awareness of where the body is (proprioception). Some people experience calming as feeling clear and focused in their mind (the physiological arousal settles so that they are able to think; however, some muscle tension may still be present).

Finding a sensory modulation strategy that works for each individual to create the 'just right' or optimal level of muscular tension and physiological arousal is important.

Creating a sense of safety

Creating a sense of safety is important for us to be able to switch off our fight and flight system, which alerts us to danger. While we are on high alert, we focus on scanning our environment for danger and prepare to escape, fight or freeze. To create this sense of safety, we can change our sensory input, seek out a new environment or modify an existing environment. Here are some examples:

- We can make sure that we are actually safe. We need to check that our alarm bells aren't activating when we are **not** in danger. This can be true in hospital environments due to fears we might have regarding other patients, hospital procedures or security (e.g. being unable to lock rooms or safeguard possessions).
- We can increase the feeling of familiarity in the environment. Novelty present in the environment keeps our senses on alert, determining whether the new information is dangerous or not.
- We can engage in sensory input or activities that provide proprioceptive and deep touch input to help increase feelings of safety and security.
- We can consider whether our existing sensory sensitivities might be contributing to feeling less safe For instance, does sensitivity to sound or diminished ability to feel connected in the environment reduce feelings of safety in crowds or noisy places? Could modifying the environment or dampening the sensory input be an effective solution?

- We can connect with a safe person, this will increase a sense of safety. Or we can use the scent of a safe person to reduce stress levels and feel calmer (Hofer, Collins, Whillans & Chen, 2018).

Self-management of symptoms

Sensory modulation can be a useful method for a person to learn to cope with or change illness symptoms. This process is referred to as self-management. Symptoms that an individual can learn to better self-manage include auditory hallucinations, pain, anxiety, depression, rumination and itch. Sensory modulation strategies work in different ways depending on the senses stimulated and also the symptoms that are being targeted. Learning to self-manage symptoms can lead to improved feelings of hope, mastery and confidence, and a reduction in distress.

People who experience hallucinations think a sensory signal is present when in fact there is none. People who experience auditory hallucinations have difficulties with auditory processing, including difficulty filtering out background noise (Farmaki, Sakkalis, Gjini, Boutros & Zouridakis, 2014). Research also indicates that people with schizophrenia and have a tendency to miss and avoid certain sensory input in the environment (Brown et al, 2002).

Sensory modulation interventions for people experiencing hallucinations may involve decreasing overall sensory stimulation so that it is easier to identify the incorrect sensory signal. For example, moving to a quiet environment to converse with someone, or using earplugs may assist a person to recognise what is an auditory hallucination and what is not. To help manage ongoing auditory hallucinations, increased auditory stimulation such as background music is useful for some people (Buccheri, Trygstad, Buffum, Lyttle, & Dowling, (2010). The development of additional coping strategies would also be beneficial, such as the trialling of a range of sensory modulation strategies to increase the options available for a person to self-manage stress levels and hallucinatory symptoms.

Sensory modulation for the self-management of anxiety could include grounding, calming and soothing sensory strategies. Common ones used in DBT for extreme anxiety include changing the temperature (by using icy water), intense exercise and self-soothing techniques.

Sensory modulation for the self-management of depression could include exploring pleasurable sensations, exercise, deep pressure and alerting or calming sensory strategies.

Increasing pleasure

Sensory modulation can change one's mood through the pursuit of something that is pleasurable. Scheduling pleasurable events is an important strategy for alleviating depression. These can include leisure activities, interacting with others or simple sensations. By participating in an activity or sensation that has the potential to be enjoyable, one's mood can shift to a more positive state. For people who are very depressed, starting with some simple sensory activities that do not require a lot of effort, time or commitment increases the likelihood of success. These may include a warm bubble bath, sitting in the garden or watching the fish in an aquarium. There is a very large range of activities that people can find pleasurable and it is important for the individual to be supported to do what is pleasurable for them. In the resources section of this book, the Exploring Leisure, Interests and Sports Through the Senses (LISTS) resource has many different suggestions incorporating a vast range of activities and interests, including the following:

- creative projects (e.g. art, craft, music, cooking and building)
- adrenaline sports or activities (e.g. rock climbing, skateboarding, bike riding, rides at amusement parks)
- activities involving other people (e.g. board games, dancing and sports)
- quiet solitary activities (e.g. meditation, birdwatching, playing solitaire).

Coping with addiction cravings

Many addictions have a strong sensory component. Substance use can change the peripheral and central nervous system, including changing the levels of norepinephrine and dopamine.

Consider some of the following substances and sensations:

- **alcohol:** relaxed body, weakened muscles, dulled hearing and impaired vision
- **nicotine:** heat, dizziness, sucking and the awareness of lungs
- **marijuana:** more intense visual, auditory, smell and taste input
- **amphetamines:** increased alertness, increased activity to seek out movement, enhanced visual, auditory, olfactory and taste input
- **caffeine:** increased alertness, increased heartrate
- **fatty foods:** taste and oral motor input

A sensory modulation approach to cravings and addictions considers the sensory patterns and preferences of the individual, as well as the sensory effects sought from using the substance. Replacement of the substance with an alternative sensation would be encouraged. Another strategy is to use a replacement sensation when the urge to use a substance is intense, as a mechanism to change the behaviour.

Reminiscing

Sensory modulation is an effective modality to promote the stimulation and sharing of positive thoughts about the past, often referred to as reminiscing. Reminiscing is used in a number of therapeutic settings including aged care and people with Alzheimer's disease, and has been shown to reduce depression and anxiety, improve memory, increase feelings of calm and promote a sense of belonging and connection. Speer, Bhanji and Delgato (2014) found that reminiscing had a positive effect on mood due to the resulting increased neural activity in the striatum. The striatum receives sensory information directly from the limbic system, and the presence of this direct pathway seems to switch on emotions and memories very quickly when sensory input is registered. For example, the smell of freshly cut grass or a particular perfume, or the sound of seagulls and ocean waves can immediately create feelings of calm and happiness, and stimulate childhood memories of summer holidays at the beach.

The senses commonly used to support reminiscing are sight, sound, smell, taste and touch. To be effective, the sensory input needs to be familiar, meaningful and pleasurable to the individual. Chaudhury (2004) goes on to recommend the value of a wider application of reminiscing beyond the elderly and people with cognitive impairment because of 'the powerful yet not fully realised potential of reminiscence as a meaningful activity'.

Sensory modulation works as a bottom up mechanism

Sensory modulation is often referred to as an example of 'bottom up processing', involving stimulation of various sensory receptors that influence central neural processing via ascending pathways from the periphery to the brainstem and cerebral cortex (Taylor et al., 2010). Therefore, sensory modulation engages the body (sensorimotor) and the emotions (limbic system) to illicit a therapeutic response. In contrast, 'top down processing' occurs via mental processing at the level of the cerebral cortex (Taylor et al., 2010), thus engaging the cognitive or higher levels of the brain. It is important to note that the processing occurring in the brain is not purely top down or bottom up as there are likely to be bidirectional pathways present. Nonetheless, the concept of bottom up processing is important to consider when there are cognitive deficits or people feel too emotional to think.

Theorists including Siegel (2011) have described an increased disconnect between lower and higher brain areas when a person is dysregulated. Van Der Kolk (2006) concludes that the brain's ability to organise a modulated behavioural response is affected by the presence of intense emotions. This is even more pronounced for individuals who have experienced significant life trauma. It appears that a person's ability to 'think their way out' of distress at times of dysregulation can be significantly compromised. Bottom up mechanisms such as sensory modulation enable an individual to alter their arousal levels and regulate emotions without needing to engage the higher brain centres. Due to the mechanism of action, sensory modulation is an effective regulation strategy even when an individual is experiencing escalated arousal states (Ogden, Pain, & Fisher, 2006). Consequently, bottom up mechanisms such as sensory modulation have been recommended for individuals with a trauma history, anxiety, agitation, anger, dissociation and hyperarousal (Sutton & Nicholson, 2011).

A practical explanation of sensory modulation as a bottom up mechanism

When we experience a sensation, such as a cool breeze or a cool touch on our skin, there are receptors in our skin that detect the sensation. These are called touch receptors. The touch receptors send information along our nerves and up our spinal cord. When the message makes its way to the first part of the brain, it has to get through the gatekeeper (thalamus). The thalamus decides which information is important enough to send up to the thinking part of the brain (where conscious awareness occurs), or to generate an emotional response (in the limbic system). This upward movement of sensory input to change emotions is, by definition, bottom up.

In a top down strategy, the thinking part of the brain sends a message down to other parts of the brain to change emotions (the limbic system) or to change body sensations: for example, thinking to oneself to 'stop feeling scared' and to mentally tell oneself to calm down.

Sensory modulation and the autonomic nervous system

Sensory modulation works on the autonomic nervous system by providing direct sensory input to it, thus increasing or decreasing sympathetic or parasympathetic activation. Sympathetic and parasympathetic systems both operate at the same time in the body, and changes to input (including sensory and motor) result in physiological changes.

Increasing sympathetic input can increase heart rate, speed up breathing and increase blood flow to the muscles and the face. This is often known as the fight or flight response. Too much sympathetic input can result in heightened stress and anxiety.

Increased parasympathetic input can improve digestion and sleep and thus is often known as the *rest and digest* response. Parasympathetic input can also be stimulated through our connection to other people. If someone else is speaking in a calm voice and has a relaxed facial expression, dilated pupils and relaxed body language, then this can trigger an increased relaxation response via increased parasympathetic activity in the ventral vagal parasympathetic branch (Porges, 2001).

The branch of the parasympathetic nervous system responsible for freezing and shutdown responses is known as the dorsal vagal parasympathetic branch. During this response, the breath and heart rate can decrease significantly. Activation of the dorsal vagal parasympathetic nervous system may be responsible for states such as shutdown, dissociation and feeling numb. An emotional state closely associated with the freeze response is the feeling of shame, which is closely associated with feeling worthless, rejected and unlovable (Lanius, Paulsen, & Corrigan, 2014).

Sensory modulation uses sensory input to change the sympathetic or parasympathetic activation. By altering this input to create an optimal amount of neural input, a person can positively change how they are feeling and enhance their functioning. These mechanisms are explored further through the concepts of the *optimal arousal zone* (Wilbargar & Wilbargar, 1997) and *window of tolerance* (Siegel, 1999; Weinstein, 2016). These concepts describe the existence of a 'window' in which a person is not too sympathetically activated (*fight or flight*) or too dorsal vagal parasympathetically activated (freeze or shutdown mode). When the neurological system functions within this window, people demonstrate an improved ability to learn, perform and connect with other people. Due to individual differences and unique sensory preferences, the optimum amount of sympathetic and parasympathetic activation will be different for different people.

Historically, most recommendations made to shift autonomic nervous system activation were based on trying to 'turn down' the sympathetic and increase the parasympathetic nervous system input to create a state of increased relaxation. However, for people who experience a decreased heart rate and slowed breathing stemming from a dorsal vagal parasympathetic freeze or shutdown response, this approach is unhelpful.

For individuals who experience decreased heart rate, slow breathing, numbing and dissociation associated with the freeze/shutdown response, increasing grounding input such as proprioceptive, deep pressure or vestibular (movement) is more useful. To illustrate this point, consider the scenario of a person who frequently feels numb and dissociated, and who at times self-harms to cope. Self-harm by cutting or burning increases sensory input and may serve to increase heart rate and decrease numbness. Sensory modulation offers alternative strategies to self-harm by increasing sensory input in a safer way. The choice of sensory input is an important consideration, as providing multiple, flooding or ineffective sensory options would be unhelpful because doing so would be too overwhelming and would not result in a calmer, safer person. The most effective sensory modulation options in these instances involve deep pressure touch, changes to temperature, proprioceptive and vestibular (movement) input.

The power sensations

Occupational therapists refer to touch (deep pressure touch and changes to temperature), proprioception and vestibular (movement) input as the power sensations. This is because these sensations generally have very strong, beneficial, and more lasting positive effects on emotional regulation and stabilisation of nervous system arousal.

Vestibular input is received through the inner ears via head movements. Direct neural connections are present between the vestibular system and the reticular activating system, more commonly known as the *sleep/wake centre*. Mathics and Bannister (2013) propose that this may be the reason why rocking, other body movements and riding in cars are so conducive to sleep. Another theory proposed by Omlin and colleagues (2016) is that vestibular stimulation through head and body motions might elicit a vestibule-respiratory response that stimulates a relaxed breathing pattern. This response has been successfully used with premature babies to 'entrain' their breathing into effective breathing patterns.

Rocking sensations are often very soothing for many different people including babies (Blackman, 2017, Bayer et al., 2011), the elderly and those with dementia (Watson, Wells, & Cox, 1998), people with heightened pain and fibromyalgia (Karper, 2013) and people with autism (Biel, Peske, & Grandin, 2009; Hartman, 2017). The sensation of rocking can be generated through a variety of activities including using rocking chairs, hammocks and baby rockers, the motion within cars, dancing, walking and many other types of movement.

Deep pressure touch is stimulated through the application of tight pressure, heavy or weighted items, swaddling or person-to-person contact. Dr Temple Grandin is a world-renowned advocate for the benefits of deep pressure to regulate emotions including the relief of anxiety (Grandin, 1992). In the 1960s, Dr Grandin invented her own 'squeeze machine', which assisted her to manage her anxiety and enhance her occupational performance. Her research studies showed the effectiveness of deep pressure to calm animals and proposed that this effectiveness was due to the input received at the level of the cerebellum. Subsequently, additional studies have demonstrated the impact of deep pressure on the nervous system, including research by Reynolds, Lane and Mullen (2015) supporting the positive effect of deep pressure stimulation on arousal and performance levels. Deep pressure was shown to reduce sympathetic and increase parasympathetic arousal in adults, and correlated with improved performance measures. Mullen and colleagues including Dr Tina Champagne (2008) specifically investigated the safety and effectiveness of using weighted blankets in a mental health setting and found them to be effective and beneficial.

Proprioceptive input is stimulated by the push and pull of muscles. Activities that can increase proprioceptive input include strength or resistance training, yoga or daily activities such as carrying heavy objects, gardening and sweeping. In recent reviews of randomised controlled trials, strength training alone was found to consistently reduce anxiety and depression levels in healthy adults (Schuch et al., 2016; Stonerock, Hoffman, Smith, & Blumenthal, 2015).

Exercise has been shown to be an effective and evidence-based treatment for depression and anxiety (Schuchet al., 2016). Exercise involves sensory input from touch, visual, hearing, scent, proprioception, vestibular and interoceptive sensory systems. It also has cognitive, psychological and social elements. Some exercise involves more intense vestibular input, such as trampolining, diving and swimming, some involves more intense proprioceptive input, such as yoga, weights training and rugby, while others involve more visual input, such as tennis, basketball and lawn bowls.

The role of the cerebellum

The powerhouse sensations of vestibular, proprioceptive and deep pressure are all transmitted to the cerebellum, with the cerebellum having strong neural pathways to the limbic system. The cerebellum plays an important role in both emotional and cognitive processing as well as modulation of the autonomic nervous system (Strata, 2015). In addition, it is now thought that the cerebellum may 'switch off' the fight or flight response and thus has a much stronger effect on emotions than previously presumed (Koutsikou et al., 2014). The cerebellar pyramis is involved in generating freezing behaviours when survival networks are activated (Koutsikou et al 2014).

The cerebellum has really only been recognised for its role in emotions in the last few years. Consequently, robust clinical research on the complete role of the cerebellum is still to be conducted and published. It is known that changes to the cerebellum are evident in people with schizophrenia, bipolar disorder, attention deficit disorder, autism spectrum disorders, anxiety and major depressive disorders (Phillips et al., 2015).

Lumb (2014) refers to the cerebellum as a 'promising target for therapeutic strategies to manage dysregulation of emotional states such as panic disorders and phobias'. It is proposed that sensory modulation be considered as a therapeutic strategy to be researched in future randomised control studies (Fitzgibbon and O'Sullivan, 2017).

Chapter 5:

Sensory Lens

Sensory Lens

There are times when individuals engage in unusual activities such as head banging, hair pulling, rocking, spinning or other behaviours. It can be useful to consider if the person is engaging in these activities to try to meet their sensory needs. This is referred to as using a *sensory lens*.

A definition of sensory lens

Considering a person's appearance, emotions, behaviour, occupations, relationships and the environment from a theoretical framework that requires an understanding of:

- the neuroscience of sensations;
- sensory preferences and processing;
- sensory modulation;
- co-regulation, and

the impact of all these on occupational performance and functioning.

(Fitzgibbon, O'Sullivan & Taylor, 2014)

In contemplating the reason or cause for an unusual activity or behaviour, it is useful to consider the following:

- could the behaviour be a type of sensory modulation strategy (even if self-destructive or unusual)?
- is the person overwhelmed by sensory input?
- did the person not notice certain sensory input?
- could they be seeking stronger sensory input?
- could the behaviour reflect the person's existing habits and ways of doing things?
- could the behaviour reflect qualities found in the environment?
- could there be physical or mental health issues?
- what are the sensory patterns and preferences?
- what are the thinking patterns?
- are there cultural or familial influences?
- is there a memory of trauma?

After identifying the likely cause of a person's behaviour, a plan for a solution can be identified. A 'cause' that is sensory can still have a 'solution' that is not sensory (such as a cognitive technique). It is also important to acknowledge that, despite the behaviour being identified as having a sensory origin or not, a sensory solution may still be an effective tool to bring about positive change. In a complex situation, it may be important to trial multiple solutions, such as the following:

- sensory modulation strategies
- consideration of cultural perspectives and norms when identifying support strategies
- changing habits
- changing the environments
- obtaining hearing aids or glasses
- medical solutions, medications, other treatments or assistive technology

- changing thoughts to positive or encouraging ones (for example,'I can stand this.')

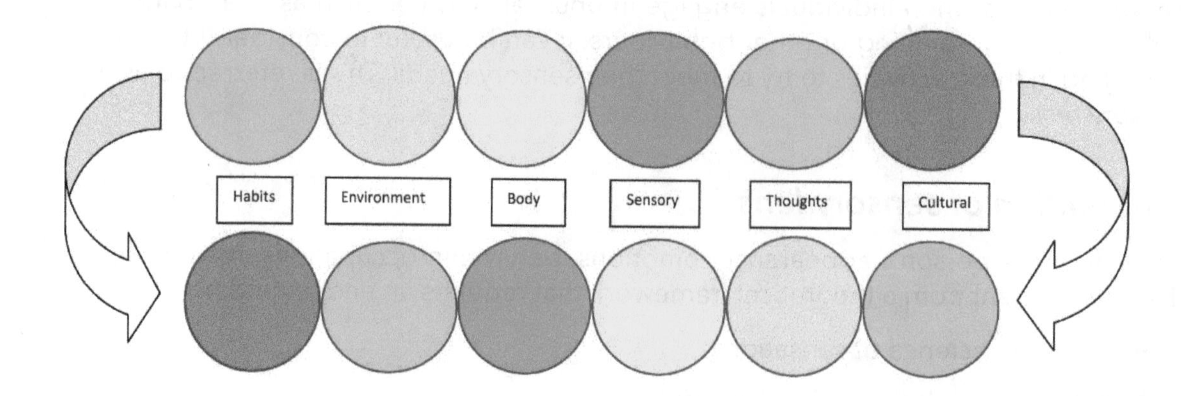

Considering causes and solutions for unusual behaviours (diagram). (2017) copyright © Fitzgibbon and O'Sullivan

To illustrate:

Anne was waiting at the front desk of a mental health services in a queue. One of the other patients was seeking administrative staff assistance. He kept pressing the bell, over and over. Anne angrily told him to stop pressing the bell. He didn't. Anne then punched him.

Later, when staff were identifying the cause of the aggression, Anne identified that she could not stand the sound of the bell.

The mental health service agreed to a plan that Anne would not wait inside the clinic near the bell. Instead, she would wait outside near the garden and waterfall. She would use her phone to inform the administrative person that she had arrived and would bypass the waiting room to attend the appointment.

In this example, sensory sensitivity was the problem; changing the environment was the solution.

To illustrate:

Fatima would pull her hair out when she was very upset and thinking about what a loser she was. She found the hair pulling painful but also grounding. Fatima was supported to trial other grounding sensations. She liked to put her whole head under a cold running water tap when she was at home. When she was out, if she became upset, she would go to the bathroom and jump up and down on the spot.

In this example, thinking was the problem; sensory modulation was the solution.

Adopting a sensory lens

Adopting a sensory lens involves consideration of the following three elements

- assessment
- interventions
- environment.

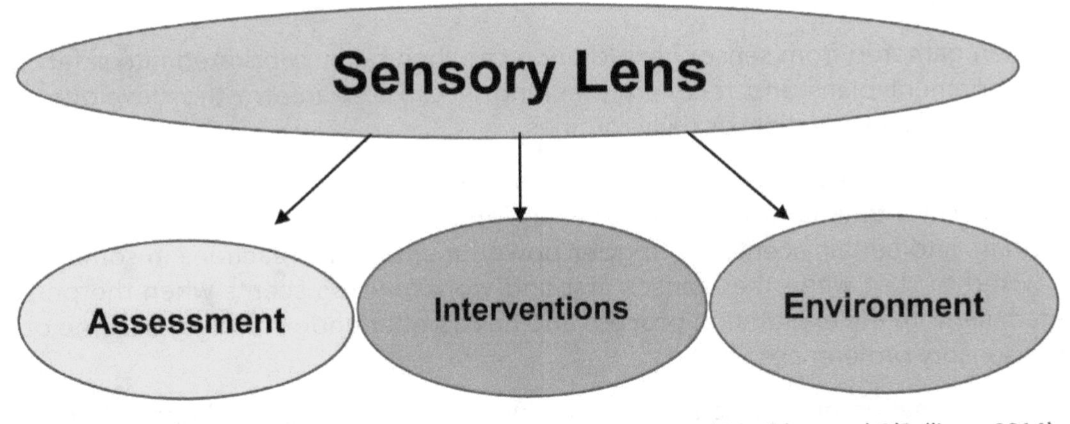

(Fitzgibbon and O'Sullivan, 2014)

1. Assessment

Sensory assessments are conducted to gather relevant information on the sensory patterns and preferences of a person and, in doing so, inform clinical formulation, the development of working hypotheses and recommendations of practical techniques and interventions to enhance functioning and improve the quality of life. There are a range of informal and formal (standardised) sensory assessment tools and methods.

Informal assessments and screening tools include self-rating tools, checklists and safety plans. Informal assessments can also involve observing a person in their environment engaging in their usual activities, to see if there are any sensory patterns influencing functioning. People can also be observed trialling different sensory items to assess their response and effectiveness.

A widely used formalised sensory assessment is the Sensory Profile (Dunn and Brown, 2002). For more information on the Sensory Profile, refer to Chapter 15 Sensory Definitions.

2. Sensory Interventions

Sensory interventions are a range of planned sensory-based strategies, programs and techniques aiming to support person's development of effective and individualised self-management skills. Examples and details follow below:

Sensory exploration

Sensory exploration is an opportunity for an individual or group of individuals to informally trial a variety of sensory-based techniques with guidance and support. Sensory exploration is always done collaboratively with the individual and includes education about the role and the mechanism of sensory modulation. There are a number of ways to initiate this process, one being to progress through the different senses starting with the sensory system most preferred or important to the person. An alternative is to start with a situation that the person wants to manage better. Once strategies are identified, the person could try it out and then discuss how it went.

Information gathered from sensory exploration can then be incorporated into safety, crisis and management plans and recovery planning. It can also inform the development of sensory kits and sensory diets or daily routines.

Note that starting with an exploration of the sense of smell is not recommended, especially for people with a trauma history. Smell has a significant connection to the limbic system in the brain, and certain scents can trigger powerful emotional reactions in some people. It is advised to start with other senses first and work towards scents when the person is more familiar with the exploration process and has a better understanding of some of their existing sensory preferences.

For more information on how to initiate sensory exploration, refer to chapter 7 on getting started with sensory modulation.

Deep pressure strategies

Deep pressure strategies include weighted blankets, lap pads, mascots, vests and wraps. If using weighted blankets and lap pads, the occupational therapist will consider and manage any risk. It is important for the therapist to familiarise themselves with this modality, its application–including with different client groups (e.g. the elderly or people with eating disorders)–and the correct procedure prior to supporting someone in the use of deep pressure strategies.

Alternatives that provide deep pressure sensory input but do not require occupational therapy prescription include using a rice bag in a pillow or cushion, using a weighted backpack, placing books in one's lap, squeezing a ball hard, kneading clay or doing strenuous activities such as yard maintenance. These can be just as effective and sometimes much more affordable and accessible.

Group programs

Group programs involve both education about and practical exploration of a range of sensory strategies to build an individual's self-management skills. They are conducted for a group of participants with guidance from one or more facilitators. Often, sensory group programs discuss each of the different sensory systems in turn, identifying possible sensory techniques and strategies related to that system (i.e. taste, sight, sound, movement, touch and smell). Participants are supported to develop goals with regard to the circumstances they wish to improve, their sensory preferences, and ways to incorporate strategies into their daily routines and coping mechanisms. Karen Moore (2016) has written some useful group programs in her book series on Sensory Connection Programs: http://www.sensoryconnectionprogram.com/workbook_chapters.php

Sensory room

A sensory room is a dedicated room with an array of sensory items and strategies for people to trial and use to support their development of self-management skills and to change their moods. In creating a sensory room, consideration is required regarding the space, colour, light, noise, furniture, equipment, etc. Levels of supervision provided for individuals using the sensory room are dependent on the organisation, the client, and the sensory equipment or items available for use.

Examples of sensory items used in a sensory room include massage chairs, lava lamps, dimmer switches, iPods with music or sounds of nature, weighted cushions or lap pads, fidget items, paper and coloured pencils, essential oils, mints or other lollies, chewing gum, picture books, word puzzles, etc. Individuals are encouraged to think about or record how they feel prior to using the sensory room, and then how they feel as they leave.

It is extremely important to promote and reinforce the transferability of sensory strategies used in the sensory room into 'real life' environments. Sensory modulation should not just occur in a sensory room–it must be transferrable anywhere with the person, otherwise the room becomes the focus, not the sensory strategy. Another important consideration that impacts on the effectiveness of the sensory room is the availability of the room. Some rooms require unlocking or a clinician to be present, which can be a difficulty when clinicians are busy or attending to other matters. Also, if another client is already using the room, it is not available for the person seeking it out. If there are obstacles to access at the time when the person needs it, then an alternative approach to a dedicated room may be warranted.

Education and training

Ensuring that clients, clinicians, support workers and family have a good working understanding of the role of sensory interventions is in itself an important component of sensory work. In the same way that increasing consumer skills enhances self-management and mastery, increasing stakeholders' sensory skill set will promote awareness, help with follow-through, give power to the techniques, and encourage others to be more mindful of their own and other people's sensory needs and patterns.

3. Environment

Sensory modulation can occur in every environment. It is very important to consider the impact of the environment and how it can change a person's emotions. An environment can be designed to create a better fit between it and the person's sensory needs and preferences.

The following environments can be considered with a sensory lens:

Mental health environment

These can include inpatient hospital, outpatient clinic and primary care and community centres. The environment can affect how a person engages in therapy, and their ability to pay attention and self-manage symptoms.

Home or community environment

These can include the person's residence (house, unit, boarding house, hostel) as well as places where they may engage in activities in the community (centres, libraries, TAFE, clubs, the workplace).

- **location**: indoor or outdoor, bright or dim, proximity to neighbours, proximity to other places and resources
- **layout**: sparse or cluttered, access to resources and materials
- **family sensory patterns**: similar sensory patterns or a mismatch?
- **own home versus shared accommodation**: private or less private with the space appearing crowded

- **access and proximity:** to community resources and activities.

Environmental modifications

- sensory spaces, corners, rooms
- portable sensory cart or case
- sensory-informed choices concerning the environment (bedroom, living room, bathroom, study space, work environment, kitchen)
- sensory additions to outdoor spaces–scented plants, herb garden, buckets of water, pot plants and grass matt on patio, wind chimes, bird feeder
- layout of the living space–organised uncluttered shelves and drawers for people who have difficulty with visual discrepancy, cleared pathways through the home for those with low registration and who bump into things, room seating where the sun comes into the room for those who prefer natural light
- considering sensory needs when building or refurbishing.

Person, Environment, Occupation (PEO) Model

The PEO model is an occupational therapy framework that describes the theory and clinical application of the person-environment-occupation interaction.

PEO consists of three dynamic components: the person, the environment and the occupation. The interconnection (overlapping region) of the three components is the occupational performance. Let us consider sensory modulation in terms of the Person (P), the Environment (E) and Occupation (O):

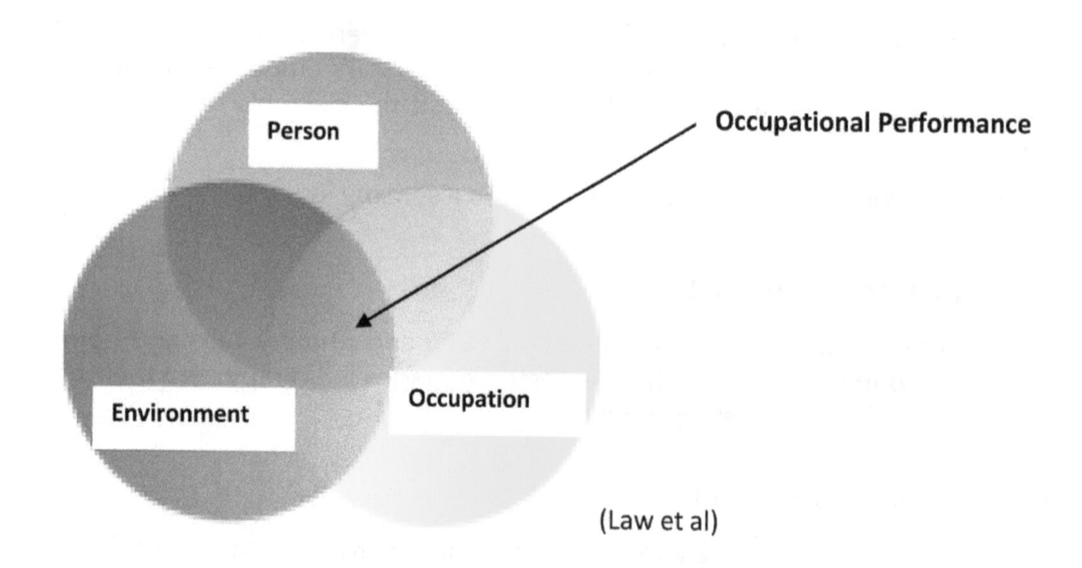

PEO model (diagram). (1996) based on diagram by Law et al.

Person

Who is the person and what are their sensory needs, patterns and preferences?

Consider the person and what sensory modulation approaches they can implement to bring about change, such as the following examples:

- changing the sensations
- changing the person's thinking
- developing a sensory-informed safety plan
- carrying a sensory kit with items that help the person feel grounded
- incorporating a sensory diet into the daily routine.

Environment

Where is the person and what are the sensory characteristics of the environment?

What is the person-environment fit?

Consider the environment and what can be adapted, such as the following examples:

- adding white noise to block out distracting sounds
- opening up a window to provide a breeze for alerting
- choosing types of sound, scents, sights (including lighting)
- considering ways for people to avoid hearing the TV or radio
- sensational spaces designed so that people can move to the area that suits their unique sensory preferences and needs at the time (e.g. a quiet zone, an active zone, a loud zone or a nature zone)
- note that modifying the sensory elements in the environment can incorporate increasing or decreasing certain sensory input to better meet the sensory needs of the individual.

Occupation

What activities, occupations and life roles is the person involved or interested in?

What are the sensory demands of these occupations on the person?

What are the relationships and social networks related to the occupation?

Consider the things the person is doing (their occupations) and what they can modify, such as the following examples:

- breaking tasks into steps
- simplifying the tasks
- adding more variety to tasks to make them more interesting (good for sensory seekers)
- making the tasks harder
- changing the types of tasks the person is doing (increasing or decreasing activity, positioning tasks indoors or outdoors, performing tasks with more or with less people, performing tasks with more or less environmental noise present)
- changing the way the person is performing their tasks (standing up, using both hands, turning the brightness down on the computer, increasing the level of initial support).

PART 2

Application of Sensory Modulation

Chapter 6:

Using Sensory Modulation Safely

Using sensory modulation safely

Sensory modulation needs to be:

- **Safe:** emotionally and physically
- **Appropriate**: age, gender, culture, identity, environment, and affordability
- **Individualised:** tailored to unique preferences
- **Meaningful:** does the person know why it is being offered? Does it make sense to them?

A way to remember this guideline is SAIM. (O'Sullivan & Fitzgibbon, copyright © 2018)

Safe

Sensory modulation needs to be beneficial for the person using it and this includes being emotionally and physically safe.

Emotional safety means that clients need to feel that using sensory modulation is not traumatising, triggering, demeaning or punitive. A sensation may be 'safe' for one person but 'noxious' for another. Many people are aware of the sensations they find aversive.

Consideration should be given to the selection of sensory items, and consulting with consumers can be valuable prior to purchasing items for an organisation.

To ensure safety from trauma and triggering, consider the following:

- some sensations can remind a person of past unpleasant memories or sensations–if a person does not wish to use a sensory item or reacts to one, then this needs to be respected by the clinicians involved
- some people are sensitive to particular sensations such as scent, noise, pressure motion (vestibular stimulation) or have difficulties modulating sensations
- scent is most safely used when an individual can control the scent: for example, when sniffing a scent in a small container; it is not safe to use aroma diffusers that disperse a scent through the whole room, particularly if a person is unable to leave the area
- some sensory items that provide weight or pressure can feel uncomfortable for some individuals.

Sensory modulation items need to be analysed for the risks involved with respect to the context in which they are being used. However, risks should also be considered against the risks of not using the sensory items. If a person is not supported in the use of a sensory item, they may miss an opportunity to benefit or may be more likely to engage in alternative coping mechanisms that have higher risks. This includes the overuse of medication, deliberate self-harm, the trauma of seclusion and restraint, and the risk of not learning self-management skills.

Risks with medication

On an inpatient psychiatric unit, medication is often used if a person is agitated, distressed or anxious.

The risks of medications include the following:

- the risk of side effects including respiratory dysfunction, hypotension. confusion or death
- risks associated with longer term use including dependence, weight gain, and metabolic syndrome
- decreased confidence in using self-management skills and the inability to transfer the use of some of the medications into a home setting because of the side effect profile (Pacciardi et al., 2013).

Risks of seclusion and restraint

The risks of seclusion and restraint have been well documented and have led to international and national policy directives to reduce their use. Risks include the following:

- trauma
- injury
- occupational and sensory deprivation
- death (from restraint)
- the breaching of human rights.

Risks of not learning self-management skills

In any clinical environment, opportunities exist for clients to learn or use strategies to self-manage their distress or agitation. The consequence of not learning new skills is that individuals miss an opportunity for self-righting and may continue their current pattern of coping that can include risky or destructive options including self-harm, assault, using alcohol and drugs, bingeing and attempting suicide. People may also be less likely to seek assistance in the future if contact with a health professional was not perceived as useful.

Safe sensory items

There are a number of sensory modulation items identified in this manual that an individual can use safely to promote and enhance self-management skills.

Sensory items that are obvious tools for self-harm, suicide or assault do not have a place in mental health facilities. However, there are sensory items that, while not obviously harmful, have been utilised in a destructive and maladaptive manner.

This manual does suggest using some sensory items that would create a degree of risk in an inpatient ward. However, these risks can be adequately managed by clear guidelines to their use and supervision. It is recommended that approval be sought from an organisation's risk management committee before sensory items are introduced into mental health or hospital settings, organisations or aged-care facilities.

Resources

The following resources list sensory items that have been used within organisations:

- 'SafeWards' is a model that is being used in many facilities. The calm down methods include sensory modulation equipment http://www.safewards.net/images/pdf/Equipment_sources.pdf
- A guide to setting up a gym facility in a mental health unit NHS, Traci Aina, 2009

- Safe Use of Sensory Equipment and Sensory Rooms in NSW Mental Health Services (2015)
- OT innovations website
- TePou Mental Health (2017). Sensory modulation as a suite of clinical tools in mental health settings
- The Environmental Programs Service Mental Health Guide by the US department of Veterans affairs (2-14) lists safe products and design for mental health units. It has a small section on sensory modulation.

This manual includes a table listing some **risks of equipment** in the resource section.

When assessing the risk of using sensory items, it is advisable to be aware of the risks of weighted modalities and items. These include weighted blankets, weighted cushions, weighted wrist and ankle bands, weights, kettle weights, weighted shoulder wraps and weighted plush toys/mascots. Additional heavy items to consider would include pets, backpacks and bags to be placed on one's lap, bags of rice and other heavy items that are available.

Weighted blankets have been used in mental health services and found to be very useful for mental health clients to reduce anxiety, agitation and to feel safe or grounded (Champagne, Mullen, Dickson, & Krishnamurty, 2015). To use weighted blankets safely, there are some risks that need to be managed effectively.

The main risks associated with weighted modalities include the following:

- suffocation from weight placed over the face
- the aggravation of existing medical issues such as poor circulation or skin integrity
- pain, including poor lifting, posture or manual handling techniques, and the risk of trip hazards if these items are left on the floor
- overheating, as many people with mental health, substance use or physical health conditions have difficulty being aware of and regulating their body temperature.

It is recommended that any weighted items used do not weigh more than ten per cent of the person's total body weight and that services purchasing weighted items limit the weight to five kilograms per item. Doing so means that most individuals (both clinicians and clients) lifting a single weight will weigh more than fifty kilograms themselves and be able to lift individual items safely. In child and youth services, items less than five kilograms would be appropriate. If a consumer is larger and would benefit from using more weight, more than one weighted item could be used at a time. It is imperative that any individual who uses a weighted item is able to remove it themselves.

A small number of deaths associated with weighted blankets have occurred, due to people being unable to remove themselves independently from a blanket, or due to the item being too heavy. Putting this risk statistic into context, there have been hundreds of deaths and thousands of injuries from seclusion and restraint and neuroleptisation (the injection of sedating medications).

Resources

Further information on using weighted blankets is available from the following sources:

- 'Weighted Blanket Guide. Everything you need to know about Weighted Blankets and Deep Pressure for Autism, chronic pain and other conditions,' by Eileen Parker and Cara Koscinski.

- Tina Champagne has information on her website, and in her book and articles.
- Risk Management Information in chapter 18.

Appropriate

Considerations for whether sensory modulation is appropriate include the following:

Age

An appropriate sensory item for an adolescent is different to an appropriate sensory item for an adult or an elderly person. Some sensory modulation items are childish looking and can result in a person feeling embarrassed or insulted.

Gender

Some clients may feel that an item should only be used by a particular gender.

Culture and identity

Cultural considerations include religious, political, race and other belief systems.

Environment

Consider privacy, noise levels, sunlight, insects and access. What is appropriate in one environment may not necessarily be appropriate in another: for example, a lounge room versus a workplace.

Affordable

In a hospital or medical environment, sensory modulation equipment may need to be durable and therefore more expensive. However, cheaper and more affordable substitutions should be available. It is important that a person can afford a sensory item if they find that it works for them, particularly so they can use such items at home. A range of low-cost options should be considered, including items found at dollar shops and op shops, and items that can be made. Sensory modulation can also occur without purchasing any equipment, through using everyday household items, natural settings and free parks and gym equipment. Innovative and inexpensive ways of making your own sensory modulation equipment are also available, with many great ideas available on the internet, Pinterest and you tube. (For example, https://au.pinterest.com/SensoryMod/)

To illustrate:

Coen is a nineteen-year-old Aboriginal man who experienced depression and wanted to quit smoking. He spoke to a nurse who suggested using sensory modulation, but Coen hated all of the items at the clinic: they were all plastic! Coen explained this to the nurse who realised that the items were not culturally appropriate or meaningful to Coen. They discussed a new plan incorporating more of Coen's interests and his love of wood and trees. Coen planned to chop wood whenever he felt angry, instead of smoking. He then took the chopped firewood to some of the elders in his community and ended up spending more time yarning with them. When he felt like smoking, he would instead play his didgeridoo.

This made him feel stronger in his resolve to stay a non-smoker as he needed to breathe well to play well.

Individualised

Each person will have different sensory modulation strategies that work for them. This is due to differences in the following

- sensory processing
- past experiences
- individual meaning attached to a particular item
- current mood.

Sensory processing differences

Our sensory systems are individualised and unique. One person may find some sensory information overwhelming (i.e. they need less input to register the sensory information) but find other sensations not strong or intense enough (i.e. they need more to register the sensory information). Having a knowledge of personal sensitivities can be valuable to better understand individual responses in different situations and environments, and ways in which to modify sensory input to improve mood and functioning.

Sensory processing differences can include the following:

- Deep touch may make one person calm and another person feel uncomfortable
- Scents may be too strong for one person and not even register with another
- Vestibular input (swinging) may make someone motion sick while it might make another person very happy–someone who loves strong movement (e.g. being on a trapeze).

Further information on individual differences and sensory processing is available in the discussions of the sensory system in chapter 3.

Past experiences

Certain sensations can be interpreted as either positive or negative due to personal experience. Sensations can often trigger memories of the past, which can illicit strong emotional responses such as in the following examples:

- a person who nearly drowned as a child may be very nervous being around pools and water
- the smell of mowed grass can be a reminder of the fun playing outside as a child with the neighbourhood children
- potted daisies may be a reminder of loving grandparents.

When exploring sensory modulation options with clients, it is very important to be aware of potential experiences that could trigger memories and intense emotions.

Current emotions

The emotion that an individual experiences in the moment (tired, excited, happy, stressed, annoyed, calm or scared) can influence how they respond to certain sensory input. Therefore, having self-awareness of feelings can help a person to determine the sensory input that they would find helpful at any given time.

Meaningful

Orientation to the purpose of sensory items is crucial for them to be meaningful. Without context, asking someone to put a weighted pillow on their lap or dunk their head in icy water could be perceived as quite strange!

Sensory modulation is more effective when incorporated into daily occupations such as work, study, leisure, housekeeping and self-care. A person is more likely to use sensory modulation if it becomes a routine in daily life, or if they use it while engaging in another activity. For example, someone who is interested in meeting other people and enjoys vestibular/movement input may join a dance class.

Considering the context of where and when person is likely to need sensory modulation enables strategies to be tailored to that situation. For example, a university student may identify that their anxiety is relieved when they use a weighted cushion, a fidget toy or the smell of vanilla pods. To use these strategies during a lecture, they could put their heavy backpack on their lap, use a textured pen to fidget with, and have a tissue in their pocket with the scent of vanilla on it.

Chapter 7:

Getting Started with Sensory Modulation

Getting Started with Sensory Modulation

Benefits are achievable for everyone by being more aware of sensory modulation and its use in our daily lives.

Sensory modulation has been shown to be useful in a variety of diverse clinical settings. Some debate has arisen regarding the competency of different clinicians and support staff to engage in sensory modulation interventions with clients and individuals. Guidance on this issue can be sought from The Australian National Recovery Framework (2013), which recommends **that clinicians be trained in 'non-forceful therapeutic crisis intervention, including sensory modulation strategies'**. This statement clarifies the position within Australia that all clinicians and support workers would benefit from adequate training in and support in the application of sensory modulation in their relevant work areas.

In addition, specialist knowledge is sometimes required and input in sensory modulation or sensory processing. Occupational therapists have additional knowledge and skills in sensory processing and the application of sensory modulation within occupations and the environment. We recommend referring to an occupational therapist if the following are required (the first four items) or observed (the fifth through the eighth item in the list):

- sensory assessment
- sensory profile
- the design of a sensory space for an organisation
- sensory modulation items are to be purchased for an organisation, program or environment
- sensory triggers to trauma
- when sensory sensitivity is impacting on occupations such as work, education or daily living
- difficulty in engaging in occupations due to sensory preferences
- when the person is engaging in behaviours that may be explained by adopting a sensory lens.

To help start using sensory modulation, it can be useful to adopt the E4 Framework (©copyright Fitzgibbon & O'Sullivan, 2017). The E4 Framework incorporates:

1. Explaining
2. Exploring
3. Embedding
4. Evaluating

1. Explaining sensory modulation to clients

Although sensory modulation is clearly beneficial to integrate into practice, introducing the concepts can be hard. Therefore, knowing how to introduce the concepts and how to 'get the ball rolling' are important.

The following suggestions may assist with adopting sensory modulation techniques in clinical settings with the specific focus on ways to introduce the concepts, and how to support the person to develop sensory-based self-management skills through education and connecting sensory modulation to meaningful outcomes.

Education

Provide education on what sensory modulation is and why it works. Ensure this is tailored to the individual's level of understanding, interest and motivational influences. Support this process by offering information in different mediums, including discussion, written information, pictures and diagrams. In practice, education is always best supported by practical application and exploration of sensory items, as the individual and clinician can both witness and experience the effects and impact of the techniques. For example, bringing along some examples of sensory items to explore and discuss when introducing the concept of sensory modulation can facilitate understanding and application.

Here are two examples of how to introduce the concept of sensory modulation to help manage stress and change emotions:

- what sort of things tend to help you cope, feel better or feel calm?
- what sort of things have you used in the past that have worked?

After the person has responded, the clinician can highlight that some of the strategies the person uses are actually examples of sensory modulation, as they engage the senses. The clinician can go on to discuss additional options that are available. Other ways to introduce the concept of sensory modulation include the following:

Involving the senses

'Many people find activities that involve their senses (touch, deep pressure, movement, sight, sounds, smell) are very helpful to feel less stressed and more in control. For example, you might find taking a warm bath relaxing, going for a walk helps you feel settled, and chewing on gum helps you focus your attention. It can be really helpful to work out what sensory activities could help you feel better and allow you to function better in your day. Can you think of any others?'

Sensory likes and dislikes

'People can have quite different likes and dislikes–this is sometimes called sensory preferences. For instance, one person may find music really helpful to relax, but another might find sound really annoying when they get upset, and may prefer doing a quiet task like drawing or sipping a hot drink. It is important to work out what your personal sensory likes and dislikes are to find out what can work best for you.'

Turning down fight or flight

'Sensory input sends a message directly to your brain to either switch on or off "fight or flight". So, a sensory activity can work really quickly to either help you feel calmer or more energised (depending on the sort of sensory input). For example, a heavy weight in your lap or doing some strong stretches in your muscles can help you feel more calm, while chewing on gum or something crunchy can help you to concentrate.'

Where it targets the brain

'Sensory modulation works in the same parts of the brain as alcohol, cigarettes and illicit drugs, but they don't have the negative consequences. It can really help to work out what sort of sensory activities might work to manage stress and cravings and help to reduce your use of these substances.'

What is soothing?

> *'Think about how to sooth an upset baby: we swaddle them, hug them, rock and pat them, sing to them softly, and offer a dummy. These are all examples of sensory modulation. We use these because we know they work. But just like for babies, different sensory modulation strategies work differently for different people. So, it is important to explore different types of techniques and activities to find out what is going to work best for you.'*

Self-righting

> *'"Self Righting" is a recovery framework designed by Helen Glover, a prominent consumer consultant and advocate. Rather than focusing on preventing a fall (i.e. a crisis or a flare-up of symptoms), Self Righting emphasises the importance of being able to "get back up" after falling down. In other words, knowing what brings a return to calm and stability for you when under stress, overwhelmed or in crisis. Sensory modulation is an effective Self Righting mechanism, because it works to change our mood through using our senses, which promotes feelings of calm, safety and grounding.'*

Orientation to available options in an inpatient mental health unit

> *'In this unit, we have a range of strategies and places for you to use if you are upset, or need a break from the noise and lights. Using your senses to change how you feel is called "sensory modulation". Try them out and see which ones suit you.'*

Connect sensory modulation to meaningful outcomes

Connecting sensory approaches to circumstances that are meaningful to the individual can assist with their integration into core self-management skills. Here are some examples of circumstances that sensory modulation can help with:

Frequent crisis presentations

Sensory modulation can help a person to manage crises and provide supportive strategies to inform crisis planning and acute management planning.

Seclusion and restraint incidents while in hospital

Sensory modulation can provide alternative options to seclusion and restraint, support the development of self-management strategies to de-escalate heightened emotions, and inform personal safety planning.

Goal of increasing independence in daily living skills including self-care

Sensory modulation can help a person develop skills and independence in daily living activities by exploring a range of techniques that can support activity engagement, for example, consideration of layout and configuration of living space, use of specific equipment and self-care products, strategies to improve energy levels and task completion (music, routines) and ways to compensate for sensory sensitivities or the missing of self-care cues.

Goal of return to work or study

Sensory modulation can assist with the development of individualised study techniques and the identification of vocational goals and preferences that match sensory needs. Sensory modulation can support concentration and attention, as well as help identify strategies to relax and wind-down. The development of a sensory diet can support self-regulation and activity engagement.

Improving relationships and parenting skills

Sensory modulation is a highly effective way of supporting healthy interpersonal relationships by assisting with emotion regulation and mechanisms for co-regulation. Examples of co-regulation techniques include physical touch (holding hands and hugging), going for a walk together, and sitting together on a couch covered with a warm blanket.

Reducing incidents of deliberate self-harm

Sensory modulation supports self-management skills by assisting a person to feel more grounded, to be able to self-soothe and to experience enhanced feelings of safety. Increasing these experiences can reduce reliance on self-harm practices.

Managing agitation and aggression

Sensory modulation assists with the management of escalated emotional states through the powerhouse sensory techniques of deep pressure, vestibular, oral motor and tactile, for example, the use of weighted items, compression wraps, muscle stretches and exercises, fidget items, movement, applying cold temperature under eyes and sucking icy drink through a straw.

Explaining sensory modulation to colleagues

To introduce the concept of sensory modulation to colleagues, you could include the following:

Ask how colleagues relax

Ask colleagues to think about what they do to relax when they are feeling uptight or how they unwind after a stressful day. Highlight that the things people naturally gravitate towards have a significant sensory component. In using sensory modulation to change our mood, it is important to acknowledge that we all find that different things work for different people, which is indicative of our unique sensory preferences. When upset or overwhelmed, do people feel inclined to note their thinking and try to restructure it to change their mood? Unlikely! People are more likely in the moment to use something sensory based to help calm down, ground or focus, for example going for a walk, making a hot drink, listening to music or eating some lunch.

Reinforce the evidence

- the research (both OT specific and general scientific research)
- the neuroscience
- trauma-informed care
- recovery, self-righting and self-management
- bottom up versus top down mechanisms
- the frameworks, policies and treatment guidelines that recommend sensory modulation as standard practice.

Case studies, positive outcomes

Discuss the positive outcomes achieved: nothing reinforces the value quite like real-life success stories! Consider keeping a record of feedback and comments gathered from people who have benefited from using sensory modulation.

2. Exploring sensory modulation

Exploring sensory modulation with the person

Exploring sensory modulation involves discussing sensory modulation or trialling equipment or items. Once an individual has had sensory modulation explained to them, they are interested in having the strategies tailored to suit them.

It is very helpful to have a goal in mind, as discussed in the previous section. The person can be asked the following:

> *Are there some areas of your life that you would like to focus on today?*
>
> *Can you think of any sensory modulation strategies you already use? You are probably using more than you realise. Let's explore what you are already using.*

When exploring sensory modulation, it is effective to incorporate at least one of the power sensations of tactile, vestibular and proprioception as these will provide the most intense physiological change.

One of the key points to understand about sensory modulation is that everyone is different. So what calms down one person may be infuriating to another person.

Think about your own sensory preferences:

- can you only sleep with the light on or off?
- do you prefer silence or background music?
- do you sleep sounder with a heavy blanket or doona, or prefer no coverings?
- do you like the television volume quite loud, but your partner always wants it turned down?

The best person to know what will work for them is the individual themselves! The clinician or support person's role is to guide and support the person to engage in exploration and consider what might work for them.

Options for how to introduce the use of sensory modulation

Many different options are available to introduce sensory modulation in practice. Below is a list to help get started, one that focuses on the goal of calming. The same process can be used with other sensory modulation goals

- exploring strategies and overcoming barriers
- self-exploration
- use the five strategies pages in this manual
- pick from ten sensory modulation options with a goal in mind
- one sense at a time
- link back to usual coping strategies
- observations on a home or community visit
- sensory space
- safety plan

- a relative with cognitive impairment admitted to hospital or nursing home
- complete an adolescent/ adult sensory profile then explore sensory modulation equipment.

Option 1: Exploring strategies and overcoming barriers

- explain the theory
- use a checklist - look at the resources in chapter16 for some ideas
- make a shortlist of items on the checklist and problem-solve any barriers to accessing the sensory items or using them in different situations.

Option 2: Self-exploration

- read about sensory modulation
- think about how you could start by using the power sensations
- look at Chapter 13: 'Five sensory modulation strategies to manage intense emotions and challenging scenarios' for more guidance on choice of strategies
- trial the sensations and write notes about which ones are most effective
- make a kit or photograph the useful strategies help remember them when you need them.

Option 3: Use the five sensory modulation strategies pages in this book

- read the strategies
- try the first five strategies that you think will be useful
- add other sensory strategies
- trial the sensations and write notes about which ones are working
- make a kit or photograph the useful strategies to help remember them when you need them.

Option 4: Pick from ten sensory modulation options with a goal in mind

- on a table, lay out ten sensory modulation items
- ask the person to pick up and try items that they think will work to achieve their desired goal or outcome (for example, wake up, feel more grounded and reduce anxiety)
- the person can write down or take a photo of the items that they have chosen
- consider laying out less items if the person finds that ten is too many.

Option 5: One sense at a time

- have a cupboard with sensory modulation items in it
- ask the person what sense they would like to explore
- take out objects related to this sense one at a time and ask if they would like to try them
- use a rating scale sheet to rate each item
- see examples of **rating scales** in chapter 16.

Option 6: Link back to usual coping strategies

- explain the theory of sensory modulation

- ask the client what strategies they already use
- ask the client if there is anything else related to their existing likes or preferences that they could try
- for example, 'You said you like to rock in your room, do you have a hammock or could you buy a fitness ball or swing chair?'

Option 7: Observations on a home or community visit

- observe the person while on a home visit or while out and about in the community
- look around the person's home and identify any items that may be useful
- observe how the person interacts and engages in the environment around them, and ascertain if sensory modulation could improve their mood and level of functioning
- explain the theory of sensory modulation
- discuss this with the person.

Option 8: Sensory space

- identify, with the person, that there is a sensory space or room available to use
- familiarise the person to the space or room, as part of orientation or a meeting agenda item
- trial some of the sensory items with them
- discuss how they can continue to use items that they personally find useful.

Option 9: Safety plan

- discuss the value of completing a **personal safety plan** (see an example in chapter 16)
- complete the safety plan with the person
- discuss how they can personally use sensory items to change their mood
- trial some of the items prior to the person needing to use them.

Option 10: A relative with cognitive impairment admitted to hospital or nursing home

- collect the person's usual soaps, shampoos, music, and other sensory items and transport them to the hospital or nursing home
- liaise with nurses regarding the suitability of these items for that environment
- explain to nurses how the person uses these sensory items, such as for self-care - 'Mrs T always likes her own soap to hold.' or 'Mr S likes to sit in the rocking chair in the late afternoon with his rug on his lap.'

Option 11: Complete the sensory profile then explore sensory modulation equipment

- an occupational therapist could complete the sensory profile to determine sensory preferences
- sensory modulation equipment could then be tailored according to these preferences
- it is useful information to understand if someone becomes dizzy or motion sick when receiving sensory input or is sensitive to scents and won't want to trial some of them
- if there is the time and resources to complete both the adolescent/adult sensory profile and the exploration of sensory modulation strategies then this would be informative. However, it is also possible to pursue the other options in this list for sensory modulation without using the sensory profile.

Talking vs trialling sensory items

Talk about sensory modulation at the following times

- if the person can process information well
- if they get it
- if there is a concern that trialling items may trigger trauma memories or symptoms or strong emotions.
- 'talk if you can and trial if you can't!'

Trial a sensory modulation item at the following times

- when the person has difficulty with processing information
- when the person is uncertain what will work
- when the person is psychotic, very emotional or acutely agitated.

Problem solving when a sensory modulation strategy is not working

There may be several reasons why a strategy, seemingly effective for everyone, may not be right for a particular person:

- physical difficulty: the person with a mobility problem who is told to go for a walk or take a shower when angry
- trauma triggers–the person feels unsafe walking alone or feels vulnerable when in the shower while in hospital
- not considered affordable or meaningful for the person
- not considered as an age-appropriate suggestion
- not seen as culturally appropriate
- sensory processing difficulties–the person may find certain sensory input too intense and other sensory input not intense enough
- individual sensory preferences–the person may have very strong likes and dislikes of particular sensory input, such as tastes, scents, light levels and visual scenery
- history–the person has tried the recommendation in the past with limited benefits
- difficulty transferring the skills into their own environment or use in 'real life'.

3. Embedding sensory modulation

Embedding sensory modulation into existing practices and routines

The following are suggestions to assist with embedding sensory modulation into practice:

- organisational paperwork
- developing a sensory kit
- incorporating sensory modulation into daily self-care routines
- considering the client's home and work environment
- encouraging participation in activities
- using technology

- education, engagement and support from significant others
- culture of sensational spaces.

Organisational paperwork

Identify the organisation's usual paperwork and then incorporate sensory modulation strategies within it. Common mental health agency paperwork includes crisis plans, personal safety plan, WRAP (Wellness Recovery Action Planning) and recovery plans.

For people who have identified a list of strategies that are useful in a crisis, consider recording them or taking a photo on the phone, or making a list and sticking it somewhere.

Developing a sensory kit

A sensory kit is a collection of individualised sensory-informed tools, activities and techniques that can be used 'in situ' to help a person positively change their emotional state. Sensory kits can be used to help a person feel more grounded and connected, to calm and soothe, to manage cravings, to feel more energised or to improve concentration and focus.

Sensory items pertain to the person's unique sensory system and to the desired outcome, such as items to help manage anxiety, feel more grounded, manage anger, and deal with cravings.

Examples of a sensory kit include the following:

- a tub of items kept at home
- a portable pencil case that can fit into a handbag or backpack
- a list of suggested sensory activities, pictures or songs
- prompts stored or apps downloaded on a smart phone.

Here are some examples of sensory items that a person may include in a sensory kit:

- chewing gum
- stress ball or fidget item
- stretchy bands
- scented candle
- flavoured tea bags
- picture of the ocean
- adult colouring activity, scribble or puzzle books
- cue cards with reminders regarding deep breathing or stretches.

Sensory kits can be prepared for use in different environments ranging from home to work. They can be portable to fit into a handbag or backpack.

Resources

- sensory kit examples on sensory modulation: Pinterest https://au.pinterest.com/SensoryMod/
- sensory kit information sheet in chapter 16.

Sensory modulation into daily self-care routines

Developed in collaboration with an OT, a sensory diet is a range of sensory strategies used throughout the day to help manage everyday stresses and demands. By incorporating the techniques into their daily routine, the person is better able to meet their unique sensory needs and maintain an optimal level of sensory input that promotes self-organisation and enhances occupational performance.

Developing a sensory diet involves the following:

Incorporating sensory input into existing daily routines:

- citrus body wash in the morning shower to wake up
- crunchy cereal to alert
- listening to music on the phone on the bus
- cold water and chewing gum to maintain focus in lectures
- going outside to eat lunch and walk around
- calling or texting a friend on the way home on the train.

Then adding additional activities into a person's routine:

- a daily walk
- reading or listening to music before bed
- muscle stretching activities throughout the day.

Resources

- sensory diet information worksheet in chapter 16.

Consider the client's home and work environment

Does the environment and occupations match their sensory preferences? What modifications could be achievable to create a better fit?

To encourage participation in activities

- including leisure, community engagement, self-development (e.g. group programs, study, work)
- consider activities that are anxiety provoking (e.g. public transport, going to the dentist, going to the shops).

Use of technology

- smart phones and tablets, apps
- picture notes and reminders
- recorded messages
- music.

Education, engagement and support from significant others

- family and friends
- mental health clinicians (doctors, nurses, allied health, private sector clinicians)
- community supports (primary care, non-government workers).

Culture of sensational spaces

- any space can be designed or adapted to be more sensory informed and better meet the sensory preferences of an individual
- see chapter 8 and 19 for more information on **sensational spaces**.

For more guidance or input, speak to an occupational therapist

An occupational therapist can provide additional expertise to expand on clinical interventions. Occupational therapists are experienced in the application of sensory modulation regarding the following:

- provision of assessment, clinical formulation and key recommendations
- provision of sensory modulation strategies
- recommendations relating to environmental modifications.

Occupational therapists will provide this specialist input with consideration of the person, their functional skills and goals, and their environment.

To illustrate

Sue often gets overwhelmed at work. She has a photo list on her phone of strategies to use while at work. This includes lemongrass tea, paperclip fidgets, the sound of the ocean on her phone, carrying boxes of photocopy paper to the machine (i.e. used as a weight).

4. Evaluating sensory modulation

At an individual level

- observe the impact of sensory modulation on the person
- seek feedback from the person regarding their feelings, ability to calm down and quality of life
- seek feedback from significant others about the value of sensory modulation
- review the person's functional outcomes, including crisis presentations, incidents of self-harm and engagement in meaningful activities.

At a service level

- record the number and types of referrals for sensory modulation input
- monitor referral outcomes
- administer pre-and post-evaluation protocols for sensory programs
- support research and evaluation of sensory modulation interventions and programs
- evaluate the use of sensory spaces and safety tools
- review functional outcomes including changes in symptoms, admissions, readmissions, crisis presentations incidents of seclusion and restraint and use of medications.

Opportunities to share outcomes achieved

- case studies presented to team, organisations and consumer carer groups

- in-service presentations to services
- service education platforms
- poster or conference presentations
- journal or newsletter articles.

Chapter 8:

Sensational Spaces

Sensory environments

Physical environments can play a significant role in positively influencing occupational patterns and performance (Champagne, 2006). The identification and modification of environmental factors impacting on an individual's sensory system can go a long way to enhance daily functioning.

People who prefer lower levels of sensory input are likely to responds better to neutral colours, silence or low sound, subtle or minimal scents, limited clutter and familiar furnishings. People who prefer a variety or high intensity of sensory input tend to seek vibrant or intense colours and images, loud or intense sound (e.g. music) and a variety of textures and scents.

Relevant environments where modifications could be of value include hospital and community health environments, home, community and school.

Sensory spaces

> *A range of areas and environments that provide a variety of sensory input to help a person change how they feel. (O'Sullivan & Fitzgibbon, 2016)*

Sensory spaces can be indoors or outdoors, large or small, dedicated or multipurpose. It is important to be able to conceptualise a sensory space as being much more than just a room. An individual can move into a sensory space when they need to, whereas a sensory room may require unlocking or clinician supervision. Examples of sensory spaces can include the following:

- sensory garden, nature space, water feature
- sensory corner, cabinet or wall or a box with a calm kit
- purposeful sensory spaces or zones: quiet zone, music zone, movement zone
- modified home area: lounge, bathroom, kitchen windowsill
- sensational space: one with lots of sensory modulation options. (quiet zone, active zone, loud zone, nature zone).

Planning

Planning a sensory environment involves consideration of the characteristics of the environment, as well as who will be using it. (For more information, see the Person/ Environment/Occupation section in chapter 5.)

The characteristics of the environment may include being near a noisy road, a busy thoroughfare, a hot sunny dusty area, or next to a stinky rubbish tip. For individuals who experience sensory sensitivity, these sensations can be particularly overwhelming or lead to avoiding the environment. For some, these sensations will trigger a range of emotions including anxiety, disgust or feeling overwhelmed.

Planning designs of houses, buildings, cities and streets can incorporate a sensory focus. Holt-Damant and colleagues completed research on planning urban environments for people with neurodiversity. Neurodiversity is defined as the 'diversity of the neurology which changes a person's interactions with the world through their senses' (McGee, 2012, quoted from Holt-Damant, Guaralda, Taylor Gomez, & Nicollet, 2013). The town planners involved in the research completed sensory mapping activities, including the identification of sensations and sensory triggers in particular environments. This concept of a 'sensory space audit' could be applied to hospitals, mental health units and centres, schools, playgrounds and nursing homes. It would be particularly useful to ask a person who is sensitive to sensory input to walk through an area and identify potential sensory triggers.

Sensory spaces audit

> *An audit or an assessment of an environment to identify present and potential sensations that may require modification or enhancement to meet the sensory preferences of the people using the space.* *(O'Sullivan & Fitzgibbon, 2017)*

An example of a sensory space audit for adolescents and adults is below. There are also sensory audits or sensory environment assessments available for children and classrooms (Kuhaneck & Kelleher, 2015; Middleton Centre for Autism, 2015.)

The rationale for using a sensory space audit is that by identifying potential sensations, changes can be made to the environment. An additional benefit is that an audit can inform an understanding of why an individual may be more emotional or behave differently within that environment.

To illustrate:

Mary was very distressed. She was within a private psychiatric hospital and she was having difficulty coping with the location of her room. Her room was located next to the kitchen and she found that the scents and noises from the kitchen were overwhelming for her. She was having difficulty calming herself and was considering leaving hospital. She had asked one nurse if she could move rooms but was refused the request as the nurse said that other people had not had difficulty with it. Then the team decided to do a sensory space audit, and the noise and scents were identified as being worse around Mary's room. A quiet room was located, and she was able to move.

Sensory spaces audit

A sensory space audit should commence with documentation of the environmental features present in the environment at that time. Next, the audit should be completed by moving through the environment, stopping in different spots every few metres and documenting the present and potential sensory input. Some examples include

- what smells are present?
- what sights? lighting? darkness?
- are there any bright lights, florescent lights or flashing lights?
- what are the usual temperatures? hot spots or cooler spots?
- what sounds are there?
- what textures are present?
- are there any water or other features that invite or repel touch experiences?
- are there any risky features? trip hazards?
- what is there that facilitates social connection?
- what is there that detracts from social connection?

- are there any features that allow someone to spin, rock, sway or swing?
- are there opportunities for movement?
- are there opportunities for rest and stillness?
- how much privacy is there?
- where do people walk through the area and are seating areas away from thoroughfares?

Modification of the sensory elements in an environment can incorporate increasing or decreasing certain sensory input, to better meet the sensory needs of the individuals who engage in that space. If these needs are not taken into account, the environment is likely to:

- be less inclusive for people with particular sensory preferences or needs
- lead to people staying away from an environment that doesn't meet their sensory needs
- have people feeling on edge or even distressed or agitated if they need to remain in the environment (imagine disliking heavy metal music but being trapped at a heavy metal band concert and unable to get away).

Designing or renovating sensational spaces

The idea of designing or renovating a space to meet sensory needs is one that is universal. If someone can design their environment, they will likely design it around their own particular sensory preferences. Examples of this would include the following:

- lounge rooms designed with textured cushions and a shag pile rug
- kitchens designed to be minimalist and with extractor fans to remove scents
- dining rooms with art on the walls, candelabras and opulent colours.

An individual who can design their own space can use sensory modulation daily to support their moods.

It can also be useful to reflect on potential conflict that can arise between people living together who have different sensory preferences. Conflict can occur between those who would prefer the television to be louder or quieter, the blinds to be up or down, or the same bath gels versus a variety. Winnie Dunn's book *Living Sensationally (2013)* is a wonderful resource to explore this concept more.

Ideally, the design or review of the design for a space would be conducted by a panel of people to consider a number of different sensory preferences. For instance, if one person designing a waiting room likes to seek out sensory input, the space is likely to have bright colours, loud sounds (e.g. music, television) and a scent diffuser! While this is likely to suit other sensory seekers, it may be too overwhelming for those who are sensitive to sensory input.

Unfortunately, it is common for hospitals, aged-care facilities, mental health units and centres to be quite unsuitable for meeting people's sensory needs. They often have music blaring loudly, the television is switched on constantly, there are no quiet areas to talk, and no space or areas to walk around in. Such situations can negatively affect a person's stress levels and ability to self-regulate their emotions or promote self-righting.

Sensory rooms

Sensory rooms are designated for the use of sensory modulation equipment. These are being increasingly used on inpatient mental health units, schools and for people with intellectual disability and autism. Equipment often includes massage chairs, weighted blankets and calming lighting and videos (Champagne, 2006). In planning a sensory room, consideration should be given to how it will be accessed by those who need it when they are distressed or agitated. Some sensory rooms are locked or require clinician supervision, and this can slow down the time to access it.

Developing sensory zones within the sensory space

Within every environment, whether indoors or outdoors, opportunities exist for sensory modulation or possibly sensory overload. One design solution is to develop a distinct sensory space or *zone* within the unit, centre, house or school. Even within the one room, there can be smaller zones. There are more ideas for zones than can fit into one space! Spaces can be designed so that people are able to move to the area that suits their unique sensory preferences and needs at the time.

Zones may include the following:

- exercise zone or gym
- calm garden zone
- massage zone
- low stimulation zone
- inspiring or creative zone
- music or auditory zone
- TV or video zone
- eating zone
- socialising zone
- soothing or comfort zone
- pet or therapeutic animal zone
- waking or pacing zone
- scent exploration zone
- reading zone
- icy zone
- game zone
- family zone (for visiting parents or children)
- sensory modulation items zone.

Resources

- chapter 19: sensory zones detailed lists
- chapter 14: equipment list
- sensory modulation Pinterest account: https://it.pinterest.com/SensoryMod/

Sensational spaces in communities

The idea of designing spaces to provide more options for sensory modulation in the community is exciting. Such spaces could provide more inclusive, less stressful and more calming environments for everyone, and include those with autism, mental illness, disabilities and sensory sensitivities.

Community spaces include the following:

- cafés, restaurants
- shops, shopping centres
- libraries
- parks
- neighbourhood centres, non-government offices
- malls
- medical centres, pathology labs, dentists' offices
- festivals, events.

An increasing number of community spaces are being designed with consideration of sensory needs. Some examples include the following:

- Brisbane North Primary Health Network is currently designing safe space alternatives for people who need a safe space to go due to mental illness, unsafe environments, and lack of inclusion. They are considering a wide range of community spaces and are including sensory approaches within this. http://www.northbrisbane.pirinitiative.com.au/wp-content/uploads/2015/03/2016_08_12-Safe-Space-Final-Report_.pdf)
- National (Australian) 7 Senses Street Day movement, which encourages neighbours to turn their streets into spaces that engage the 7 senses. (http://www.7senses.org.au/)
- dance parties and music festivals are creating chill-out zones for people who need a break from the sensory stimulation
- in NSW, the town of Bellingen is designing a program to consider children's sensory needs in the community. 'Bellingen Sensory Friendly Safe Spaces' (http://www.bellingen.nsw.gov.au/news/funding-success-sensory-friendly-safe-spaces)
- art galleries are becoming multisensory environments, with more exhibitions designed to provide different visual, auditory and visual experiences. Some also have low-sensory viewings (e.g. GOMA in Brisbane).

The sensory benefits of nature and the outdoors

Records found as far back as ancient Egypt, China, Greece and Persia discuss the healing and restorative qualities of nature. Other healing places such as hospitals and monasteries also included elements of nature. (Velarde et al., 2007). Studies of gardening programs show positive psychosocial benefits for those with mental illness, including addictions. They report a reduction in agitation, depression and stress levels (Gonzolez & Kirevold, 2014).

Theories of why nature improves mental health are listed below.

SRT (stress reduction theory)

Natural environments help reduce stress more than artificial ones due to the role nature has played in our evolution. This is attributed to the fact that certain natural landscapes (grassy plains, treed areas, winding rivers) provided our ancestors refuge, physical advantage and safety (Bratman et al, 2015). Therefore, our instinctive preferences for these environments stimulate a positive physiological and affective response including within the parasympathetic nervous system. This theory is supported by research studies that show positive changes in anxiety, rumination and negative mood when people are exposed to these environments (Ulrich, 1981; Ulrich et al, 1991).

The relaxation response

Several studies (Grahn & Stigsdotter, 2003; Hartig et al., 2003; Ulrich, 1991) show that contact with nature improves recovery from stress and enhances attention and concentration. Studies also reveal participants self-report increased feelings of relaxation with exposure to nature.

Environmental self-regulation hypothesis

Korpela et al. (2001) has studied the connection between restorative experiences, self-regulation and place attachment. Nature settings were the preferred favourite places and strongly correlated with positive feelings of relaxation, forgetting about worries and self-reflection. Studies have also shown that physical activity in natural settings improves positive emotions, self-esteem and behaviours more than physical activity in built environments (i.e. outdoors versus shopping centres).

Attention restoration theory

Nature invokes a sense of 'fascination', 'being away' and 'compatibility', which Kaplan and Kaplan (1989) suggest replenishes attention and may improve memory.

Strong connection between nature and health with the following major benefits

- relaxation, restoration and stress reduction
- faster recovery response gained by natural stimuli versus built settings (Ulrich et al, 1991)
- reduction of mental fatigue and improvement in mood (Alcock et al 2014)
- renewed attention and positive affect leads to increased sense of wellbeing (Berto, 2005)
- enhanced functional outcomes including recovery from surgery, reduced pain levels, better work performance and higher job satisfaction (Frumkin, 2001)
- Improved concentration and reduced impulsivity in adults and children with ADHD (Taylor, 2011)
- engagement in an enjoyable and normalising activity
- overview effect: views of nature (mountains, canyons, waterfalls or a star-filled night sky) create feelings of wonderment and awe. Research shows that such feelings can alter our experience of time and increase feelings of unity, connection, patience and

a desire to help others (Rudd, Aaker & Vohs, 2012)

- blue space 'visibility of water'- a study showed that contact with blue space (in this study it was visibility of the ocean) is associated with reduced levels of psychological distress (Nutsford et al, 2016)
- can promote engagement in other activities involving physical movement, tending to plants or animals, reading, sketching, social engagement
- crosses age, gender, disability and cultural barriers–people of all ages, backgrounds, cultures, and ability and disability levels. All can find a way to connect to nature in some way
- movement promotes gross motor development for children
- pleasant surprises in nature like unexpected butterflies, birds and flowers.

Nature can incorporate the following:

- open spaces, courtyards, playgrounds
- community gardens, green spaces, parkland
- potted plants, hanging gardens
- sensory trail (more structured sensorial 'journey' with different senses sequentially stimulated)
- views through windows
- animals (e.g. guinea pigs, aquariums, chickens).

Sensory systems engaged by nature and the outdoors

Touch: breeze, temperature, warmth or cooling, feeling underfoot, the feel and texture of leaves, flowers, grass, tree bark, moss, water, dirt, the feel of a bench or other furniture, patting animals, campfires, water features, tending to plants

Sight: sun, sky, clouds, level of light, trees, foliage, patterns, water features, surrounding movement, butterflies and insects

Sound: water trickling, wind chimes, a breeze in the foliage, bird calls, crunching of leaves underfoot

Smell: water, air, leaves, flowers, cut grass, compost, herbs

Taste: edible gardens, picnic in a park, bush tucker, BBQ, toasted marshmallows

Movement: walking, reaching for items to touch, swing, balancing, feet in water

Deep pressure/proprioceptive: sitting on grass or against a tree, walking in leaf litter or sand, balancing rocks, digging, building, and gardening

Interoceptive: deep breathing (deep inhalations if effort induced, or relaxed gentle breathing if resting), the feel of one's heart rate, the feel of muscles (exertion or relaxed), swallowing cool water.

Here are some opportunities when in nature or the outdoors to engage in heavy work activities

- pushing, pulling, lifting, playing, moving, digging
- squeezing, pinching, digging/ throwing (Jennifer Gay, 2012).

Ways of incorporating nature and outdoor sensory input into practice

Consider first:

- previous interests and engagement
- current influences or factors impacting on engagement (money, proximity, anxiety or trauma background, paranoia, sun and temperature sensitivity).

Then:

- explore interests and preferences
- go outdoors: local walks, visit a space
- investigate local options to engage with (walking groups, community spaces, city farms)
- link with another person to enhance motivation and social engagement
- views and sounds of nature: windows, posters, pictures, photos, as well as recordings of nature (evidence that looking at scenes of nature increases activity in parasympathetic nervous system, and the more meaningful or awe-inspiring the picture, the better the response)
- engage in community activities (e.g. bush regeneration)
- incorporate nature into personal spaces (pot plants, rocks, shells, leaves, water features).

A great document outlining the vast benefits of nature for health and wellbeing is *Beyond blue to green: The benefits of contact with nature for mental health and wellbeing*. It is available on line at http://www.deakin.edu.au/data/assets/pdf_file/0004/310747/Beyond-Blue-To-Green-Literature-Review.pdf

Chapter 9:

Sensational Activities

Sensational Activities

Sensational activities are pursuits that people participate in that involve the senses. The sensory input of a specific activity can change a person's feelings in the moment. Exploring and planning for activities that will meet a person's sensory needs can be a valuable intervention. Activities can include leisure, sports, exercise, art, craft, music and games. A list of **individual activities** is available in chapter 17.

On an organisational level, supporting people to engage in activities to facilitate sensory modulation is a viable intervention approach. Organisations need to be mindful that people respond to sensory input differently so consideration of individual needs is always recommended. Organisations that would benefit from sensational activities include:

- community centres
- schools
- nursing homes
- mental health units.

Activities could include those with a focus on movement, sound, scent, taste and touch. Ideas for sensational activity groups could include the following:

- making sensory kit activities
- soap making
- arranging pot pouri
- making fudge and other food treats
- creating a box of favourite scents
- making face masks
- applying lip balm, hand cream
- using stress balls
- playing with putty or slime.

Activities that promote movement to stimulate awareness of body in space (proprioception and vestibular input) include the following:

- tai chi
- juggling
- dance
- yoga
- zumba
- resistance classes
- circus
- swimming.

The following are creative activities that stimulate or soothe the senses:

- art
- gardening
- clay
- karaoke or singing
- cooking or baking groups

- listening or playing music.

Some sensory modulation activities are not suitable for mental health units. See the section on risk and adhere to local policies.

Consideration should be taken to make sure activities have the following attributes:

- SAIM: Safe, Appropriate, Individualised and Meaningful
- voluntary (e.g. participants can opt in or out according to sensory needs)
- suitable for those who are sensitive to sensations
- suitable for those who are seeking a variety or intense sensations
- affordable for the person to use in the long term (or a cheap substitute is available)
- does it connect to a meaningful activity? is it meaningful? (e.g. squeezing a stress ball vs. kneading pizza dough for dinner)
- can the sensory items assist the person to engage in a meaningful activity?

A list of **sensory modulation items and equipment** is available in chapter 14.

To fund sensory items, consider the following:

- donations from families or the community
- sensory drives (ask for donations specifically after Mother's Day, Christmas, or at other times when people may have been given presents that don't meet their sensory needs)
- compare the cost of medicine and clinician injuries to the cost of the sensory items
- whether clients should pay a small fee so they can take some sensory items home with them
- a budget for items that need replacing
- homemade sensory items: see Pinterest or other websites for great ideas.

Chapter 10:

Using Sensory Modulation to Address Healthy Living

Using Sensory Modulation to Address Healthy Living

Sensory modulation can be used to effectively promote healthy living habits.

Many theories exist about why some people don't engage in healthy habits despite access to plenty of information and advice indicating that they should. Using a sensory modulation approach, a possible explanation as to why some people overeat, consume cigarettes, alcohol and other substances is that they are engaging in these behaviours to try to change how they feel. This is illustrated in the common phrases of people 'drowning their sorrows', and 'eating comfort food'. As an alternative, by substituting a more constructive sensory input, people have an option to self-manage their emotions rather than using the unhealthy habit to do so.

Unique sensory preferences can have a significant impact on an individual's health and lifestyle such as the following:

- people who are sensitive to movement and loud sounds may enjoy a particular activity but avoid participating because they are conducted in large groups, or the venue may be too crowded
- someone who enjoys the 'spin' of tobacco may benefit from doing another activity that creates 'spin' in order to cease it
- someone who prefers high levels or increased variety of tastes, or has difficulty discriminating more subtle, subdued flavours may be more likely to seek out foods with high sugar or salt content to meet their sensory needs.

Therefore, understanding our sensory system can really assist with healthy lifestyle choices and the development of lifestyle goals that are tailored to the individual.

Three lifestyle goals that are worthy of consideration include the following:

- sensory modulation and healthy eating, healthy food choices
- sensory modulation and leisure engagement
- sensory modulation and substance use or misuse.

1. Sensory modulation and healthy eating

Nutrition and healthy eating has long been an issue for the mental health population, and a wealth of literature exists around the reasons for this (including increased appetite due to medications, reduced energy and motivation levels, lack of knowledge around healthy eating, socioeconomic factors, the use of food to relieve boredom and pass time, and lack of engagement in other meaningful activities).

Another factor could be the possible influence of sensory preferences and needs on the food choices and eating habits of individuals.

More often than not, eating food is not just about physiological nourishment. An additional consideration is 'what sensory needs might be being met by specific food choices?' as shown by the following examples:

- to calm: foods that are found to be soothing, comfort foods
- to alert: assist with concentration–strong flavours, crunchy, textures
- to alleviate distress or boredom: particular tastes, increased quantities
- to assist with grounding and orientation to the present: strong or aversive flavours

and textures

- to create pleasure: foods that are found to be enjoyable.

While these are all valid reasons why an individual may eat certain foods, challenges can arise due to the following:

- the food choices people make (quality)
- the quantities of foods consumed.

To illustrate

Sally had a chronic psychotic illness and her antipsychotic medication (Clozapine) has contributed to a noticeable weight gain over a twelve-month period. Sally had been provided with dietetic input and was prescribed on medication to manage her pre-diabetes status.

The occupational therapist wondered if taking a sensory-informed approach to the problem would be warranted.

Initially, education was delivered to explain sensory approaches. Then exploration commenced regarding the times when Sally wanted to feel calm, and the times when she wanted to be more energised.

Sally identified that the types of foods she consumed when wanting to feel calm and soothed were ice cream, chocolate, high cream milk and vanilla cake. These foods were notably sweet tasting, soft and smooth-textured items.

The types of foods Sally consumed when she wanted to alert and energise herself were peanut M & Ms, Pringles and other chips (especially salt and vinegar), all notably with high-taste and crunchy textures.

Strategies discussed with Sally

Choosing alternative foods that delivered the same sensory needs but reduced calorific intake were identified:

- for calming: skim milk with malt, vanilla and caramel flavoured teas, low-fat flavoured yoghurts
- for energising: crunchy vegetable sticks with yoghurt-based dips, flavoured rice crackers, citrus teas
- exploring alternative sensory strategies other than food (such as scents for calming and alerting, scented body lotions and hand creams, textured fidget toys and craft activities)
- development of a sensory plan with identified strategies that reflect her sensory preferences and needs
- exploration of additional physical health activities to address weight gain and assist with stress management (such as daily exercise goals).

The benefits of using this approach for healthy eating and lifestyle management include the following:

- provision of a different way of looking at healthy eating and food choices
- assistance to people to identify alternative options that still meet sensory needs
- person centred and driven: strategies are very unique and tailored to the individual.

2. Sensory modulation for leisure and activity engagement

Could there be a sensory explanation as to why an individual engages in particular activities and leisure pursuits, and have different and particular interests? Some examples include:

- people who seek out movement and vestibular input may be drawn to activities that involve movement, speed and testing the limits (e.g. sports, running, dancing, rock climbing)
- outdoor activities might be more appealing for those who like visual sensory input (colours, light) or a particular touch (feeling of the sun and wind on the skin, temperature)
- activities like yoga and tai chi may be more appealing for those who crave proprioceptive input to feel calmer and centred in themselves.

Our unique sensory patterns may also impact on the activities that an individual may not be interested in or perhaps actively avoid, such as in the following examples:

- people who are sensitive to temperature, sound or light may engage more in indoor activities or activities where they can easily modulate the sensory input (listening to CDs over live music, watching DVDs over going to the movies)
- solitary activities involving less people may be chosen over group leisure pursuits for people who are sensitive to movement, noise and crowds.

Therefore, an understanding of sensory preferences can help us choose activities that better meet our sensory needs, as well as adapt activities or the delivery of activities to increase our participation, enjoyment and mastery.

To illustrate

Mostafa expressed an interest in using gym equipment to help with energy levels and to work on his fitness and confidence, but he was very sensitive to noise and intensely disliked the feeling of heat/sweat beading and running on his skin. Options discussed with Mostafa included the following:

- attending the gym at less crowded times
- using headphones or earplugs to block out the environmental noise
- choosing a gym with air-conditioning
- remembering to frequently wipe down with a towel
- work out at a home gym while wearing wet clothes
- consider finding a gym with a swimming pool.

To illustrate

Libby enjoyed the smell of fresh herbs and flowers and liked the idea of growing and tending to her own, but found touching soil and having messy hands very distressing. Libby was encouraged to do the following:

- start with small potted plants or aquaponics
- use gardening gloves
- tend to a small gardening plot initially, and increase the size when comfortable to do so.

To illustrate

Ben was keen to participate in a local community art class. However, in the classes he had a lot of difficulty sitting still maintaining focus on the activity and was distracted by surrounding noise and the movement of participants around him. This led to a lot of disruptions for others in the class, as well as frustration for Ben as he was not progressing with his art work. Strategies trialled included the following:

- Ben going for a long walk outside prior to the class
- Ben's spot in the class was moved to a less central position (less distraction for him or others)
- being provided with the option of alternating his body position throughout the lesson (from standing up at an easel to sitting while doing his artwork)
- using a weighted item in his lap or around his shoulders while engaging in his art.

Resources

There are a number of worksheets and checklists that occupational therapists can use to help explore leisure and activity engagement from a sensory perspective:

- Tina Champagne workbook: Sensory Modulation and Environment: Essential Elements of Occupation, 3rd Edition Revised. Explores sensory modulation applications, theory through practice https://www.pearsonclinical.com.au/products/view/363
- Tina Champagne website: http://www.ot-innovations.com/
- Karen Moore website: http://www.sensoryconnectionprogram.com/author.php
- http://www.therapro.com/Life-Skills/The-Sensory-Connection-Program.html
- LISTs (Leisure Interests Sports Through the Senses) written by Carolyn Fitzgibbon.

3. Sensory modulation for substance use or misuse

Sensory modulation can be a useful adjunct to other therapies for substance use and misuse. Sensory modulation can be used in several ways including:

- understanding why a person may be using the substance
- using sensory modulation strategies as an alternative to the substance
- understanding the sensory aspects of the habit patterns
- using sensory modulation strategies to build new healthy habits
- using sensory modulation strategies when experiencing an urge or craving for the substance.

Understanding why a person may be using the substance

People give many reasons for using substances, and one of them is the effect of the substance on the body and mind. Substances are a type of sensory modulation strategy in that they involve sensory input through taste, ingestion, smell, sniff, smoke, inhalation, injection or swallowing.

Common reasons that are given for using substances include the following:

To obtain pleasure

- to get high
- to get a buzz
- to feel increased sensations.

To relax or decrease muscle tension or intense emotions

- to relax
- to numb
- to feel sedated
- to feel 'out of it'
- as a strategy to manage anxiety, numbing, anger, dissociation.

To feel more alert or focused

- to feel alert or awakened
- as a strategy to manage dissociation.

It is useful to ask an individual what they are getting out of using the substance, or why they started using it in the first place.

Sometimes substances are used to shift a feeling, such as an emotional state. This commonly includes using substances when feeling down, depressed, stressed, anxious, sad or angry. The emotions that are often preferred in these states include being calm, happy, numb, exhilarated, less stressed.

Using sensory modulation strategies as an alternative to the substance

Sensory modulation strategies can be used to substitute for the common reasons that substances are used. Most sensory strategies will not offer as intense a sensation; however, some people find that they are useful.

1. To obtain pleasure

Increasing intense sensations:

- visual: watch very intense visual YouTube clips (e.g. the splendour of kaleidoscopes, the world's most satisfying videos)
- taste: eat very flavoursome food
- auditory: listen to new music (favourite genre).

To feel happy:

- pleasurable activities or sensations that we enjoy (e.g. playing with the dog, birdwatching, chai tea).

To feel exhilarated:

- adrenaline sports or watch exhilarating movies.

To increase adrenaline:

- intense exercise
- use cold water and breath holding to invoke dive reflex

- adrenaline sports
- jump into an icy pool, waterfall, partake in an ice bucket challenge.

2. To relax or decrease muscle or mental tension

Numbing:

- spinning, intense exercise, humming breath.

Calming:

- taking a bath, doing yoga, going for a walk, exercising, placing a weight on lap
- hammock, swing chair, surfing.

To reduce stress:

- activities that calm breathing or relax muscle tension (e.g. exercise, bath, massage).

3. To feel more alert or focused

Alerting sensations:

- exercise: aerobic or resistance, chewing crunchy or chewy food, having slushy ice drinks, applying cold water to the face, icy spray.

As a strategy to manage dissociation:

- heavy weight in lap, pushing muscles against resistance, exercise, chewing, icy water.

4. Substitute with a sensation

A driver for ongoing substance use can also be the sensations created from the activity, such as the mouth sensations, smells, sights and sounds. Sensory modulation can be used as a substitute for these sensations. First, it is necessary to identify the specific sensory aspects of the substance use that are enjoyable or motivating, and then a similar sensory input can be used as an alternative.

Oral motor

What mouth or oral sensations are derived from the substance use?

- for example, chewing, blowing, sucking, sipping, cool or hot in mouth.

Sensory modulation oral motor strategies include the following:

- chewy food, crunchy food, strong flavours, mints, hot drink, cold drink, food.

Scent

What scent or nose sensations are derived from the substance use?

- for example, sniffing, inhaling, hot or cold temperature, scent.

Sensory modulation nose or scent strategies include the following:

- inhaling steam, hot herbal drinks, Vicks inhaler, tigerbalm cream, scent–mint, lemongrass, rosemary, lemon.

Touch

What touch sensations are derived from the substance use?

- for example, rolling a joint, holding a glass, having the skin pierced, relaxed muscles, tense muscles, flushing, coolness, hypersensitivity

Sensory modulation touch strategies include the following:

- rolling a fidget toy, shelling nuts, holding a non-alcoholic drink, holding a warm or hot towel, having a warm bath, touching different textured fabrics, having a cold shower, fidgeting items, using a hand-held massager.

Movement

What movement sensations are derived from the substance use?

- for example, dizziness, spin, lack of coordination, more coordination?

Sensory modulation movement strategies include the following:

- spinning around on a chair, dancing, circus, gym equipment.

Visual

What visual sensations are derived from the substance use?

- brighter, blurry, more intense, sharper?

Sensory modulation movement strategies include the following:

- YouTube videos, kaleidoscopes, art, lava lamps.

Understanding the sensory aspects of the habit patterns

When a habit is developed, the brain packages together a sequence of steps. To illustrate this concept, imagine a person eating dinner, clearing away the dishes, pouring a glass of wine and sitting on the deck to relax. If they want to cease drinking, they will find that they will have an urge to drink after they clear away the dishes after dinner. The brain will want to engage in its normal habit, and will send some strong thoughts and sensations to remind of the next steps in the sequence. By developing an understanding of the habit patterns, it can be easier to consciously change the sequence.

Common habit patterns involve the following:

- places where the substance is obtained or the habit commences (e.g. kitchen, smoking area outside work, nightclub, car)
- people (e.g. smoking friends at work, husband and wife drinking wine on the deck, group of friends using ecstasy)
- changes to our body (e.g. stress, lethargy, anger)
- sensory prompts (e.g. the smell of coffee, the sight of wine in the fridge, a shelf hiding the box with marijuana in it, loud nightclub music)
- times or routines of the day (morning tea, 5pm)
- activities (e.g. driving, dancing, movies).

Using sensory modulation strategies to build new healthy habits

To change a habit intentionally, first write down all the steps in the sequence. Then identify the steps where change could occur and what that change could be.

Some examples of changes to steps could be the following:

- To break the habit of wine after dishes clearing - Arifa eats dinner, then asks her flatmate to clear away the dishes, then goes straight to the bathroom and runs a bath with the lights low and calming music playing
- To break the habit of ecstasy use with group of friends - Manny does not go out with his 'ecstasy' friends at night at all. He trials seeing some of the friends individually at cafés or going to the movies during the day with them.

Using sensory modulation strategies when experiencing an urge or craving for the substance

Full withdrawal from a substance may require medical supervision or a detox unit. After the withdrawal is completed, or after it has ceased (for a mild substance), cravings or urges to use the substance will still exist. Urges or cravings are intense thoughts and physical sensations associated with not completing a habitual use of a substance.

Sensory modulation strategies can be used in the following circumstances:

- to assist with managing the physical sensations associated with the urge
- (e.g. tense jaw–chew dried apricots; hot flushes–apply icy water to face)
- in an urge coping box–a box with sensory modulation items and reminders of why you want to cease the substance (e.g. money, pictures of a holiday you can have with the money saved)
- to distract from urges (e.g. computer game, playing a musical instrument)
- increase healthy habits overall (e.g. exercise, eat well, drink new herbal teas)

Resources

Refer to chapter 13 resources including;

- changing how you feel: cigarette cravings
- changing how you feel: substances
- changing how you feel: feeling numb
- changing how you feel: panic, anxiety and stress.
- changing how you feel: grounding
- changing how you feel: anger and agitation

Refer to chapter 16 resources including:

- changing substance use with sensory modulation
- self-soothing worksheet
- intense sensations worksheet
- to develop new leisure interests, refer to LISTS in chapter 17

To illustrate

Jared enjoyed smoking marijuana while he played his computer games in his bedroom. He was using more and more marijuana each day and studying less until eventually he failed his university course. Jared decided that he wanted to quit smoking marijuana. He had a strong association between playing his computer games and marijuana use but still needed to use his computer to study. He decided to change where he used the computer to support habit change. He moved his computer to the lounge room, which was used by other family members. He wrote out a timetable involving full days at university with time each day in the study centre. While studying, Jared would squeeze a hand grip strengthener, which helped him feel less anxious and reminded him of his goal to get his hands strong so he could get back into rock climbing. Jared deleted all of his marijuana drug dealers from his phone and avoided his friends who were marijuana users. Jared joined a dusk beach volleyball group at university. He would then go home, have dinner with his family and watch TV with them. Jared found that his urges were highest when he was in his bedroom, and he organised to swap bedrooms with his brother.

Chapter 11:

Future Opportunities

Future Opportunities

Future uses

Sensory modulation could be used in many different settings and applications in the future:

- police, ambulance and fire officers could assist people who are intensely agitated or distressed
- schools could assist students who are distressed or not concentrating
- universities could have icy water available in the room outside of exams
- adult mental health inpatient units: spaces could be designed to include sensory modulation strategies with zones for low stimulus and for calming; sensory modulation equipment could be provided for individuals to use when they feel that they need it
- emergency departments and hospital wards could have a wide range of sensory modulation equipment available
- workplaces could provide weighted shoulder wraps and noise-cancelling headphones to assist people to work more efficiently
- dentists could use weighted cushions to calm nervous patients
- could be used in the case of natural disasters or traumatic incidents to reduce shock
- could be used to help people experiencing grief and loss
- could be used as a standard treatment modality for chronic pain clinics
- could be provided to women during childbirth
- community spaces could be designed to be inclusive for all community members and promote neurodiversity.

Future research

This is an exciting time in health. Information is emerging all the time regarding neuroscience, neuroplasticity and the mind-body connection in promoting health and wellbeing. It is anticipated that future research may also pave the way for investigating sensory processing patterns (including sensitivities) from a biological perspective. This includes the role of the gut in sensory processing and the bio-balance approach. As is the case with most new and innovative therapy interventions, the time between the publication of newly acquired evidence and its transference into standard service delivery can be lengthy. This is an inherent frustration for clinicians and service providers who, in their day-to-day work, witness the value and benefit of interventions such as sensory modulation, but are waiting for the increasing depth and levels of evidence to support their observations.

Therefore, the growth and acceptance of sensory modulation as an evidence-based practice will further increase with continued emphasis on research, to reinforce its practical application from theory into practice.

Chapter 12:

Conclusion

Conclusion

Evidence for the effectiveness and value of sensory modulation is resoundingly clear as it is a recovery-oriented and trauma-informed practice utilising bottom up strategies and increasing self-management and self-righting options.

Sensory modulation is beneficial as an intervention in its own right, or as a component of other therapies. It can be used to decrease the intensity of emotions so that a person is able to stay present and engage in psychological therapy or use cognitive strategies. Therapeutic group participants can use sensory modulation strategies to stay alert and increase their attention and the amount of information absorbed.

In this manual, sensory modulation strategies have been provided for a range of emotions, experiences and urges. The recommended first options to explore are the power sensations of proprioception, vestibular/movement and touch. Sensory modulation needs to be safe, appropriate, individualised and meaningful to the individual.

In inpatient units, community clinics, non-government support services or primary care services, sensory modulation strategies can be easily embedded into existing practice and care models. Design of spaces can include low stimulus areas and zones with sensory modulation equipment.

Locking away sensory modulation equipment creates a barrier between the client needing it and when they can use it, as accessibility is dependent on staff availability. Using everyday, inexpensive and safe items that can be left unlocked can be a solution to this issue.

Sensory modulation is used by many people each day to change how they feel, often without realising it. With greater knowledge of and focus on sensory input, it can be used by more people in their day to day lives. Individuals can use this resource manual to be able to self-right, manage emotions, connect with others and to engage in meaningful occupations. In doing so, a person can enrich their life, living a life with increased quality and meaning.

PART 3

Sensory Modulation Resources

Chapter 13:

5 Sensory Modulation Strategies to Manage Intense Emotions and Challenging Scenarios

Five Sensory Modulation Strategies for Managing Intense Emotions and Challenging Scenarios

These worksheets are also available in PDF at http://sensory-modulation-brisbane.com/

Password: ChangeHowYouFeel

The following section outlines a number of challenging scenarios and intense emotional states where sensory modulation may be useful to alleviate distress and enhance functional outcomes. For each scenario, five sensory tips are suggested. Trialling these sensory tips will assist a person to get started with sensory modulation, build confidence and promote active self-management skills. As proficiency and confidence increases, additional sensory modulation strategies can be explored and included.

Many of the sensory modulation strategies suggested for each scenario will overlap and be effective for more than one emotional state, because they are strongly based on the power sensations of:

- proprioception
- vestibular
- tactile

Each of the five strategies recommended are followed by a number of examples in dot points. These are provided to offer further explanation and insight into each strategy. The examples may be ideal for the individual, or may not be suitable and so alternative options may need to be explored with the person.

Each intense emotion or challenging scenario is also illustrated by an example case study to further explain and provide context to the strategies recommended.

It is important to always remember that all sensory modulation strategies need to be:

- **Safe:** emotionally and physically
- **Appropriate:** age, gender, culture, identity, environment, affordable
- **Individualised:** tailored to the persons unique preferences
- **Meaningful**: do they know why it is being offered? Does it make sense to them?

Change how you feel: panic, anxiety and stress

1. Use cold temperature to evoke the mammalian dive response

- use a cold gel pack, a zip lock bag or sink filled with water or cold wet washer, placing over eyes and holding breath. Note: this is contraindicated for people with heart problems or anorexia.

2. Reminder of a loved one or loved place:

- the smell of Dad's aftershave
- the smell and taste of basil as a reminder of their garden at home
- a photo or familiar object as a visual or touch reminder

3. Something heavy to rest in the lap:

- books
- pet
- weighted cushion, bag of rice

4. Moving the body:

- jumping on the spot or dancing to music
- rocking in a hammock or rocking chair
- movement through yoga or tai chi poses
- mouth movements like chewing gum or sucking an icy drink through a straw

5. Pushing muscles against resistance:

- stretching or pushing against a wall or piece of furniture
- squeezing something firm or pulling a piece of exercise elastic or material

To illustrate:

Due to her anxiety levels, Ruby has been unable to use public transport for some time. With the help of her occupational therapist, Ruby was supported to create a sensory kit full of items she could utilise while waiting for and travelling on the bus, to help her manage her anxiety. Items in the kit included:

- chewy mints
- a sports bottle with icy cold water
- smart phone with photos of her and her pet cat
- stretchy coloured hair bands and beads to fiddle with

Ruby made sure her backpack was in her lap, providing deep pressure input. She also tried to regularly move as well as tense, hold and release muscles in her arms and legs to maintain a feeling of connection to her body.

Check: Are the strategies SAIM? Safe, Appropriate, Individualised, Meaningful?

Change how you feel: grounding

It can be useful to feel grounded when experiencing dissociation, disconnected, flashbacks or feeling spacey.

1. An intense sensation, including:

- clapping hands together hard or rubbing skin firmly with a hand washer
- sucking a sour lolly or warhead or smelling something strong (e.g. eucalyptus, rosemary)
- listening to loud music
- temperature, like squeezing ice in hand or crunching it in teeth, or a hot shower

2. Something heavy to rest in the lap:

- books or backpack
- pet
- weighted cushion or bag of rice

3. Work through the senses, by identifying:

- 5 things you can see
- 4 things you can hear
- 3 you can feel
- 2 you can smell, and 1 you can taste.

4. Moving the body:

- stretching
- rocking in hammock or rocking chair
- dancing to music
- moving through yoga or tai chi poses

5. Pushing muscles against resistance:

- compressing joints, holding and releasing
- stretching or pushing against a wall or piece of furniture
- squeezing something firm or pulling a piece of exercise elastic or material

To illustrate:

James found when he was very stressed or overwhelmed, he felt numb and had the experience that he was outside of his body. He found these sensations disturbing and scary as he felt like he was losing control. To feel less numb and bring himself back, James would engage in self destructive behaviours like punching himself, and to escape the unpleasant feelings he would use alcohol or smoke cannabis. As an alternative, James was introduced to less destructive intense sensations to help his brain and body feel more connected. He preferred sucking a very sour lolly and the smell of tea tree oil. James also found that intense exercise (jumping on the spot, shadow boxing) and holding strong stretches in his arms also helped him to re-connect to his body.

Check: Are the strategies SAIM? Safe, Appropriate, Individualised, Meaningful?

Change how you feel: anger and agitation

1. Use cold temperature to evoke the mammalian dive response

- Place a cold gel pack, zip lock bag filled with water or cold wet washer over eyes and holding breath (note: this is contraindicated for people with heart problems or anorexia).

2. Moving the body:

- star jumps, leg lifts or push ups
- rocking in chair
- bouncing a basketball

3. Pushing muscles against resistance:

- large arm movements: painting a wall, wall art with chalk
- pushing against a wall or piece of furniture
- digging a hole with a spade

4. Carrying or sitting with weight:

- weight in lap or on shoulders
- carrying a load of books or water buckets
- weighted cushion, bag of rice

5. Muscle tensing and releasing:

- tense muscles as slowly breathing in, let tension go as slowly exhale
- squeezing a stress ball or a hand grip

To illustrate:

Katie's difficulty controlling her anger was detrimental to her relationships with friends and family. Though she was mostly able to avoid outbursts in the workplace, she could feel her anger building throughout the day. She realised she was more likely to act on these pent-up feelings at the end of the day when her resilience and energy were lower, and in situations where she felt targeted or under pressure (like a difference of opinion with her partner or a misconstrued comment). Sensory modulation strategies that Katie adopted to help her manage her anger included:

- engaging in sensory modulation activities every lunch break to help promote a sense of calm and reduce stress levels (taking a break, a walk outside of the office, and cool pack on eyes)
- listening to her favourite music on the way to and the way home from work
- squeezing a stress ball during work meetings or work telephone calls helped her remain calm when feeling stress levels increase
- 5 to 10 minutes of yoga stretches and poses in the evenings (sometimes Katie's partner would also join in!) to help wind down and feel more relaxed

Check: Are the strategies SAIM? Safe, Appropriate, Individualised, Meaningful?

Change how you feel: self harm

It can be useful to make up a kit of strategies or reminders of the following strategies to assist with self harm or self destructive urges.

1. An intense sensation:

- clapping hands together hard and rubbing skin firmly with a small towel
- sucking a sour lolly and smelling something strong (eucalyptus, rosemary)
- listening to loud music
- temperature, like squeezing ice in hand or a hot shower

2. Deep pressure input:

- weighted items
- stretchy wrap or blanket held tightly around shoulders or body
- tight fitting clothing: leggings, jeans, beanie, gloves

3. Moving the body:

- stretching, star jumps and leg lifts
- moving through yoga and tai chi poses
- dancing to music

4. Pushing muscles against resistance:

- pushing against a wall or piece of furniture
- squeezing clay or tennis ball firmly

5. Reminder of a loved one or loved place:

- Mum's jumper, shampoo or perfume
- smell of forest or ocean
- Photos or videos

To illustrate:

After a bullying incident at school, Tammy started to scratch and cut her thighs to alleviate tension and deal with painful feelings of diminished self-worth and rejection from members of her peer group. To help Tammy develop alternative ways of managing distressing emotions, the following sensory modulation strategies were identified:

- intense sensations Tammy could engage in at school: Instead of self harm, Tammy would draw or sketch with a hard black pencil, suck a cold drink through a straw, splash cold water on her face and hold her breath. She was also encouraged to regularly use the gym to do some intense exercise and use weights. Sometimes smelling her grandfather's aftershave or looking at photos of her friends was also helpful.
- sensations at home: when at home, Tammy would go for a powerwalk, have a hot shower, dig in the garden and water the plants with a heavy watering can, do some yoga practice, and listen to her favourite loud music.

Check: Are the strategies SAIM? Safe, Appropriate, Individualised, Meaningful

Change how you feel: for people with dementia

1. Access to items that are familiar and meaningful to help soothe and calm:

- cushion, throw rug, framed photo or picture
- personal ornament, religious or spiritual symbol
- specific soap or perfume

2. Use of sensory modulation to assist with self cares:

- weighted item on lap if distressed
- soapy hand washer or sponge to squeeze during shower time
- favourite music or radio in background during meals

3. Identify behavioural patterns, known triggers, and episodes of agitation or distress to implement sensory modulation:

- meaningful activity e.g. watering the garden in the afternoon when becomes more agitated
- using knitting or fiddle muff to occupy hands when family return home after a visit
- regular movement activity or walking to help promote feelings of calm and grounding

4. Where possible utilise sensory items that are a true representation rather than an abstract painting or object:

- pictures of nature, or picture of garden or pet at home, weighted mascot of a dog

5. Use powerhouse sensory systems of movement and deep pressure to facilitate calm and reduce distress:

- rocking chair, hand massage, weighted cushion or heavy rug in lap

NOTE: Sometimes an adult with cognitive impairment will appear fatigued, yawning and less responsive when their sensory system (especially vestibular) is actually hyper-aroused (Champagne, 2016). At these times, reduced levels of sensory input (reducing noises, environmental activity) and supervised powerhouse input like deep pressure (blanket on lap, squeezing a pillow) will help to achieve a more regulated state.

To illustrate:

Yoshi is an elderly man with dementia, who recently moved to an aged care facility. Nurses at the facility noticed that at 3pm every afternoon, Yoshi became increasingly agitated and restless and was observed to wander to the doors in an attempt to leave the facility. When redirected back to his room or a chair, he became more upset, would return to the door and sometimes lashed out at nurses. Rather than escorting him back to his room, on one occasion one of the nurses went for a walk with Yoshi around the facility and outside in the gardens. This sensory stimulation (including movement, light, colour, sound) helped Yoshi to settle significantly, and afterwards he returned to his room without incident. From that day, Yoshi was supported to go for a walk every day at 3pm, and often other residents joined in the activity. It was discovered not long after this activity was initiated, that when Yoshi lived at home, he walked his dog in the local park at 3pm every afternoon.

Check: Are the strategies SAIM? Safe, Appropriate, Individualised, Meaningful

Change how you feel: enhance feelings of safety

1. Make sure the environment is safe

- putting locks on doors and bars on windows can create a sense of safety or bells hung on the door or windows so that it can be heard if someone enters.
- reduce shadows and fast movement, and be able to scan the environment easily (e.g. remove places where someone could be hiding)
- access to a phone

2. Keep a light on at night

- rather than negatively impacting on sleep, it can increase feelings of safety and security and improve sleep

3. Use of safe scents and sounds

- smells and sounds that have positive associations with places (e.g. using salt, sand or seashell to remember a holiday) or people (e.g. partners deodorant, mums shampoo, voice recording of friend)
- white noise machine to dull everyday sounds
- having no headphones on in certain environments to be able to hear any approaching danger

4. A dog

- a dog can help with feeling safe. Dogs scan the environment for danger. They also would fight back if necessary

5. Deep pressure

- tight clothing
- tight sleeping bag, stretchy sleep bag or heavy doona
- weight on lap

To illustrate:

Michaela was having trouble sleeping in her new home. She woke up to every little sound and was fearful that someone would break in. She told her mum about her worries, and put a lock on her door. She used a white machine app on her phone so that some of the sounds were duller. She watched the fish in her aquarium before she drifted off to sleep.

Check: Are the strategies SAIM? Safe, Appropriate, Individualised, Meaningful

Change how you feel: cigarette cravings

1. Mouth (oral) sensations

- taste: lemon juice, mint, ginger, peanuts, sour lollies, chilli, coconut, salty foods
- heat in mouth: ginger, chilli, hot tea, coffee, hot mints, mouthwash, toothpaste
- sucking a sour lolly
- sucking: drinks through a straw, lollies, carrot stick, chuppachup, beef jerky, smoothie, juice, slurpee.
- blowing: balloon, straw in cold drink, bubbles, blow cotton balls across table

2. Heat in lungs

- turn on hot shower and breathe in steam
- hot drink - breathing in the steam

3. Holding and rolling:

- fidget with paperclips, phone, peel peanuts, crack pistachios, origami, stress ball, rubix cube, plasticine, or press fingers together hard

4. Spin:

- stand up and spin around
- spin on office chair or roundabout
- swing
- roll head around

5. Calming

- jump up and down
- walking
- push ups
- weight on lap

To illustrate:

Cooper wanted to stop smoking and decided to make up a craving kit for his backpack. He put into this some beef jerky, pistachio's to crack, a men's magazine to remind him of his goal of improved physical fitness and a picture of the office chair, to remind him to spin around on it. He also filmed himself on his phone, telling himself why he wanted to give up smoking. He planned to watch this video if the cravings got too intense.

***Check*:** Are the strategies SAIM? Safe, Appropriate, Individualised, Meaningful?

Change how you feel: pain

1. Change temperature

- hot packs heated safely or electric hot water bottle
- cold gel packs
- ice spray
- dencorub, eucalyptus rub, tiger balm or other muscle heat ointments

2. Vibration

- vibrating cushion
- hand-held massager (or electric toothbrush)
- massage chair insert or foot massager

3. TENS machine

- Transcutaneous Electrical Nerve Stimulation (TENS)

4. Deep pressure

- massage or rub the affected area
- use deep, sustained pressure into the muscle fibres
- tight clothes e.g. thermals, leggings, exercise garments

5. Swinging, rocking

- hammocks
- swing chairs
- rocking chair

To illustrate:

Jedda was very overwhelmed with her back pain and had trouble getting out of bed in the morning to go to work. She started the day with a warm bath and then applied dencorub. She did half an hour of work on the computer and then would do soothing activities for half an hour. This included the TENS machine, stretches, or using her heat pack. She kept alternating sensory modulation techniques with doing tasks that she needed to get done. In this way, she was able to feel a sense of achievement at the end of the day, and that her life could get back on track.

Check: Are the strategies SAIM? Safe, Appropriate, Individualised, Meaningful?

Change how you feel: difficulty sleeping

1. Stand by bed

- stand by the bed in the dark, until feeling the need to sit down. Then lie back down in bed

2. Icy water to invoke dive reflex

- using cold temperature to evoke the mammalian dive response. Use a cold gel pack, zip lock bag or sink filled with water or cold wet washer, place over eyes and holding breath. Note: this is contraindicated for people with heart problems or anorexia
- this strategy is particularly useful if feeling anxious or just woken up from a nightmare

3. Change the room or the bed

- adjust the temperature e.g. open the windows, turn on a fan, put on a doona, cold or warm face washer, or a heat gel cream or electric hot water bottle.
- if experiencing night sweats, try sleeping in thermals that will absorb the sweat without feeling cold. Or try a chilly towel.
- use a white noise machine or slow music or ear plugs
- eye mask to block light

4. Deep Pressure

- use a weighted cushion prior to bed
- do some stretches
- sit with the dog on the lap

5. Swinging, Rocking

- hammocks, swing chairs, floating bed, in-yard swing, rocking chair before bed.

To illustrate:

Mohammad was a police officer and often woke up sweaty and with his heart racing after a nightmare. He tried to use breathing techniques to get back to sleep but this was not working. He learnt about sensory modulation techniques and decided to do a yoga routine prior to bed to let go of the day's tension. He wore thermals to bed and slept with the windows open so that the room was cool and he could use his doona. Mohammad found that if he used a sound machine all night to make white noise, that he would not wake up startled by little noises. Just before sleeping, he stood beside the bed in the dark until he was tired. He usually went to sleep quickly. He also knew that if he had bad nightmares that he was able to go to the fridge and get out his cold water zip lock bags to put over his eyes and hold his breath. This calmed down the adrenaline quickly and got him back to sleep much faster.

***Check*:** Are the strategies SAIM? Safe, Appropriate, Individualised, Meaningful?

Change how you feel: cravings for substances

1. Mouth (oral) sensations

- taste: lemon juice, mint, ginger, peanuts, sour lollies, chilli, coconut, salty foods
- heat in mouth: ginger, chilli, hot tea, coffee, hot mints, mouthwash, toothpaste
- sucking: drinks through a straw, lollies, carrot stick, lolly pop, beef jerky, smoothie, juice, slushy drink
- blowing: Balloon, straw in cold drink, bubbles, blow cotton balls across table

2. Use a sensation whenever there is an urge to use

- exercise, jump up and down, spin
- intense scent (mint, eucalyptus, basil, strong perfume, aftershave)
- music
- hand massage or use a grip strengthener
- read a magazine

3. Use other sensory modulation strategies, worksheets or resources

Identify what you need and then refer to relevant information:

- calming sensations
- intense sensations
- numbing (spinning, exercise)
- adrenaline sports or sensations
- pleasurable sensations
- changing habits

4. Redecorate to change triggering environmental cues

Change the place where the substance was consumed if it is in our home.

- face the bed in a different direction
- place a craving kit box on the table where the smokes used to be kept
- change the location of glasses, drinks in the fridge
- remove the chair that was used to sit in and consume the substance and change around the other furniture in the room

5. Plan new habits to replace substance habits

Create new habits to replace the old ones.

- musical instrument
- exercise
- craft
- cook
- refer to LISTS worksheet for further interests (chapter 17 resource section)

To illustrate:

Fran had been through a detox program and was going home committed to not using alcohol anymore. She asked a friend to accompany her home from the program and stopped at the shops on the way to buy some sensory items. At the shops she bought beef jerky, fresh ginger, four different types of fresh juice and four new teas to try. She also bought a five kg bag of rice to use as a weight, some new gym clothes and books. When she arrived home, Fran put these items onto a shelf which she called her 'coping shelf'. She then gave the friend all of her alcohol, wine glasses and CDs that were associated with drinking. Fran had already made a plan to see a friend a day straight after work for the next two weeks while she got used to being home again. She drove home from work a different way so that she did not drive past the bottle shop. Every day without alcohol she felt stronger and stronger.

Check: Are the strategies SAIM? Safe, Appropriate, Individualised, Meaningful?

Change how you feel: waiting room design

1. Consider the wall colour, artwork and décor

- not too crowded
- calming colours
- artwork that is not too bright, busy or confronting

2. Living greenery

- pot plants, flowers, hanging garden on wall
- fish tank

3. Access to cool drinking water

4. Availability of inexpensive, low risk sensory items for use while waiting

- fidget items (spongy stress balls or small material pouches filled with rice)
- ear plugs
- magazines
- puzzle books, adult colouring books etc.

5. TV channel alternatives

If there's a TV, use recorded videos to reduce the risk of content being overwhelming or triggering for people. For example:

- documentaries about nature or historical buildings
- interesting activities in local area

To illustrate:

Jorg is in the waiting area of a community clinic to see his doctor. The doctor is running a bit late so he has to wait longer than expected. Jorg tends to find environmental noise (i.e. people talking, radios, TV, opening and closing doors) and visual movement (i.e. people walking in and out) quite overwhelming in these situations, especially when he is already feeling stressed. These experiences increase his agitation and restlessness and in the past he has walked out without attending his appointment. Jorg now uses a number of sensory modulation strategies to help him feel more at ease in the waiting room environment, including:

- earplugs to dampen down background noises, or
- listening to his preferred music on his smart phone with a headset
- flicking through a magazine to keep his hands busy
- looking at a large poster on the wall of a person fishing on a riverbank

Check: Are the strategies SAIM? Safe, Appropriate, Individualised, Meaningful?

Change how you feel: feeling numb

People who experience intense and overwhelming emotions sometimes want to feel numb from their emotional pain. The numb feeling has been described as thinking less, or not feeling the emotion (including the physiology of the emotion). Some people identify that they use substances such as codeine or alcohol to feel numb. These strategies can be used as an alternative to using substances or to create a feeling of numbness:

1. Changing temperatures

- alternating cold showers with warm showers
- immerse self in or rub icy water over body and then have a warm bath
- go under a waterfall, ice bucket challenge

2. Humming Breath

- put ear plugs in, or hold fingers over ears to close them. Then hum loudly on the breath out. This will provide a vibration feeling around the sinus area

3. Spinning

- spin around in circles
- go on a roundabout or other playground equipment

4. Lengthy intense exercise

- dance wildly
- run for a long time

5. Other intense sensations

- refer to the intense sensation list in chapter 16

To illustrate:

Michael liked to take codeine so that he could feel numb and not feel his emotions anymore. His Therapist had suggested relaxation but he didn't want to feel anything. He just felt so bad about himself that sometimes that he just wanted relief from emotions. He decided to try sensory modulation strategies. At work when he had urges to use codeine, he would race up and down the internal stairs two at a time during his break. He also went to the bathroom and spun around and around. After work he went to his local pool and swam laps and alternated the pool with warm showers. At home he would also listen to music or use the humming breath.

Check: Are the strategies SAIM? Safe, Appropriate, Individualised, Meaningful?

Change how you feel: auditory hallucinations (A.H)

1. Change or leave that environment

- are A.H worse in noisy environments or quiet environments? When other people can be seen or when there is no one else?
- how much privacy is there? Can a blind be placed over the window so that no one from the street can see in?
- do walls need to be soundproofed? Or can a white noise machine mute background noise?
- does it help to sleep with the light on?
- are there specific locations when the A.H are increased or decreased?

2. Auditory input

- try humming breath - Put ear plugs in, or hold fingers over ears to close them. Then hum loudly on the breath out. This will provide a vibration feeling around the sinus area
- decrease other auditory input with ear plugs, noise-cancelling headphones or white noise.
- increase other auditory input with music, layers of sound, TV, singing in a choir

3. Something heavy to rest in lap

- books, pet, weighted cushion or bag of rice

4. Moving the body

- jumping on the spot, dancing to music, movement through yoga or tai chi poses
- rocking in a hammock or rocking chair,
- mouth movements like chewing gum or sucking an icy drink through a straw.

5. Using cold temperature to evoke the mammalian dive response

- Use a cold gel pack, zip lock bag or sink filled with water or cold wet washer, place over eyes and holding breath. Note that this is contraindicated for people with heart problems or anorexia

To illustrate:

Paul noticed that his auditory hallucinations were worse when he was at the noisy shopping centre. He decided to buy his food online even though it was more expensive. When he was at home he thought that the people at the bus stop were watching him through his window. He put a heavy blind over the window and used YouTube to get some white noise in his unit. He found that in a low light with no sounds from the outside world that he stopped feeling on edge. He liked to put a heavy cushion on his lap and complete a crossword. He found that his A.H were much less problematic for him overall.

Check: Are the strategies SAIM? Safe, Appropriate, Individualised, Meaningful?

Chapter 14:

Sensory Modulation Equipment and Items

Sensory Modulation Equipment and Items

When choosing equipment it is important to remember that it is:

- Safe
- Appropriate
- Individualised
- Meaningful

For more detailed information on this, refer to chapter 6 on using sensory modulation safely.

Sensory modulation does not require that equipment is purchased. Many useful items can be found within the home environment, can be inexpensively made, sourced from cheap shops, or from nature.

Examples of these items are listed under the budget item category.

Equipment list:

Sensory Items for TASTE and ORAL MOTOR

Budget items

- mints
- sugarless chewing gum
- sour candy
- lemon lollies
- straws for drinking
- ice and icy cold water
- singing, humming and whistling exercises
- using herbs and spices in cooking activities
- warheads
- singing activities e.g. choir.

Additional items

- bubble mixture
- recorder
- flavoured teas
- diet cordial
- chewy and crunchy snacks.

Deluxe items

- harmonica
- pan flute
- juice machine
- slushee maker
- chocolate moulds
- cooking groups
- gardens with fresh herbs, vegetables, edible flowers.

Sensory items for SIGHT

Budget items

- photos, pictures cut out of magazines, from webpages post card pictures
- crosswords or sudoku from webpages or cheap shops
- mindfulness colouring in activities (web or Kmart)
- poems, inspirations writing
- swatches of colours, paper, pieces of material
- DVDs or U-tube videos of nature
- magazines
- bubble wands
- gardens, fountains, flowers.

Additional items

- lava lamp
- art and photo books
- different pot plants
- fairy lights
- nature documentaries
- puzzles
- games e.g. cards, board games
- art and craft activities
- train or sports DVDs e.g. surfing.

Deluxe items

- dimmer switches
- wall projector
- iPad with internet access
- bubble columns
- aquarium
- bird bath
- waterfall
- disco lighting
- fire pit
- computer games
- iPad with visual apps
- virtual reality goggles
- nail art
- yarn activities.

Sensory items for SMELL

Budget items

- scents from the garden - lavender, herbs, lime leaves, flowers, bark, mulch, grass
- scents from the bathroom: soaps, hand wash, eucalyptus rub, perfumes, bath gels, shampoo, and moisturiser
- scents from the kitchen: vanilla essence, mint, baking cookies, mustard, coffee, coconut, citrus fruit, stone fruit, and cinnamon
- herbal teas.

Additional items

- homemade soaps, lavender bags
- incense
- essential oils (can be diffuse in cups of warm water or drops on cotton wool)
- moh doh.

Deluxe items

- electric oil diffuser
- perfume
- scent infused heat bags
- perfume making kit
- essential oils
- massage oils
- fresh flowers
- gardens with fresh herbs
- kit with scents
- variety of soaps, body washes and shampoo.
- nil odour.

Sensory items for MOVEMENT

Budget items

- exercise cards
- stretching cards
- dancing to music
- bouncing ball
- exercise ball, fitness ball
- skipping rope
- juggling balls
- stretchy exercise bands
- drawing, painting, clay art materials
- mindfulness colouring books (or download from internet)
- exercise mat.

Additional items

- balance ball
- balance board
- bosu ball
- ribbon on stick
- tai chi and yoga DVDs
- dance DVD (e.g. Bollywood)
- drums
- slack rope.

Deluxe items

- rocking chair
- hammock
- swinging chair
- walking garden maze
- wii (e.g. dance game)
- dance
- rowing machine
- garden e.g. digging potatoes
- swimming pool
- sand ball area
- gym equipment
- basketball hoop
- table tennis table
- in-yard swing.

Sensory items for TOUCH

Budget items

- zip lock bag to fill with cold water
- gel pack (hot or cold)
- instant ice pack or instant heat packs
- sipping hot drink or cold drink
- bag of rice or heavy books in lap
- soft cleaning mitt, face washer or soft towel
- textured cushions
- hand or body lotion
- eucalyptus rub
- stress ball
- clay
- textured items
- rubix cube
- stretchy wrist wrap
- velcro
- sea shells, pebbles, seeds, bark.

Additional items

- heat wheat bag
- hand-held massager
- weighted neck wrap
- stretchy wrap for shoulders
- spray ice
- hand grip strengthener
- heated blankets
- guinea pigs, chickens
- soft scarves
- bubble wrap
- moh doh.

Deluxe items

- weighted items - lap pads, cushions, wrist weights, weighted knitted chickens
- massage chair or massage mat for chair
- sleeping bag
- massage oils
- vibration mat
- foot spa
- leatherwork, clay
- woodturning lathe

- electric blanket, throw rugs and quilts
- kinetic sand
- sink with icy water
- squeeze machine.

Sensory items for SOUND

Budget items

- clapping, tapping rhythmic exercises
- whistling, singing a song, humming
- sounds of nature (ocean waves, waterfall, rain, storms, wind, birdcalls)
- music (instrumental, singing, classical, jazz, native music)
- relaxation CDs
- ear plugs
- homemade rain maker.

Additional items

- wind chime
- white noise machine, CD or app
- rain maker
- CD players.

Deluxe items

- noise-cancelling headphones
- ear defenders
- background noise muting earplugs (sonic defence)
- drums and other musical instruments
- iPod and iPad loaded with music
- sound proofed areas
- acoustic tiles
- karaoke machine
- DJ turntables.

Resources

- further ideas are available at the sensory modulation Pinterest account: https://it.pinterest.com/SensoryMod/
- risk management information is available in chapter 18.

Chapter 15:

Sensory Definitions

Sensory Definitions

There are many related concepts and terms used in conjunction with sensory modulation, many of which are referred to in this manual. This chapter provides detailed definitions for a number of these concepts, including sensory modulation.

Sensory modulation

Sensory modulation encompasses two distinct but related concepts, one relating to the neurological process, and the other relating to the intervention.

1. a neurological process

> *Sensory modulation is 'the capacity to regulate and organise the degree, intensity, and nature of responses to sensory input in a graded and adaptive manner. This allows the individual to achieve and maintain an optimal range of performance and to adapt to challenges in daily life' (Miller, Reisman, McIntosh & Simon, 2001)*

2. an intervention

> *Sensory modulation is changing how you feel through using your senses. (Fitzgibbon and O'Sullivan, 2013)*

An additional definition of sensory modulation as an intervention is used in the Australian National framework for recovery-oriented mental health services (2013). It states that sensory modulation

> *involves supporting and guiding people (often in a designated sensory room) to become calm or shift an emotional state by using sensory tools such as sights, sounds, smells and movement, or modalities such as weighted blankets or massage chairs.*

Reference to sensory modulation in this manual is related to the intervention or strategy that an individual is supported to use.

Sensory processing

Sensory processing refers to the ability to take in the information receive from the senses, both external and internal, and then use that information to function effectively. Specifically, the body sends information from the senses to the brain through neural pathways, which are much like roads. Once the information reaches the brain, it is interpreted, and then the information can be acted on.

Sensory processing involves several steps:

- **detecting** the sensory information (noticing it, not noticing it, or noticing too much)
- **filtering** the sensory information (the thalamus filters out a lot of sensory information and if too much or too little is filtered out, this can cause difficulties)
- **discriminating**, or noticing the differences between sensory information
- **organising** sensation, or making sense of the information to organise action (sensory modulation)
- **completing** a task, or doing something in response

Difficulties with sensory processing occur in some people with Autism. The 2013 Diagnostic and Statistical Manual of Mental Disorders, 5th Edition (DSM-5) refers to the following sensory processing difficulties:

Hyper or hypo-reactivity to sensory input or unusual interests in sensory aspects of the environment, for example:

- apparent indifference to pain or temperature
- adverse response to specific sounds or textures
- excessive smelling or touching of objects
- visual fascination with lights or movement.

Occupational therapists understand that there are people without a diagnosis of autism who also have sensory difficulties. There is currently extensive debate about whether a diagnostic label for people who experience difficulty with sensory processing (such as Sensory Processing Disorder and Sensory Discrimination Disorder) is warranted. Further information on this concept can be found at the following - https://www.spdstar.org/basic/founder-dr-lucy-jane-miller

Difficulties in engaging in daily life due to sensory processing difficulties may be assessed and treated by an occupational therapist. It is useful to be aware that each individual has a unique pattern and preference for processing sensory information. However it is possible to use sensory modulation strategies without specifically being aware of an individual's sensory processing. The most important factor to be guided by is the individual themselves and their distinct preferences.

Sensory preference

Occupational therapists consider that sensory processing exists on a continuum, with people's individual differences on this continuum being reflective of their unique sensory preferences. For example, some people are very sensitive to smell, most people are middle of the range, and some people are not sensitive to smell at all. By getting to know our own individual sensory preferences we can apply this information to our daily lives and situations. Instead of interpreting sensory preferences as a sign of dysfunction and necessitating remediation, occupational therapists view them as markers of our unique sensory systems. This provides an opportunity to adapt and accommodate to these preferences, to enhance occupational performance and improve quality of life. The occupational therapist Winnie Dunn (2001) describes sensory differences as not problems to resolve, but rather that living a satisfying life is the real challenge to address.

Sensory profile

A standardised sensory assessment developed by Dunn and Brown (2004) with separate assessment tools for the adult and adolescent population, and for children. It measures sensory preferences (sensory processing patterns) across the domains of taste and smell, vision, auditory, touch, activity and movement. Information generated from the assessment conveys patterns in functioning across four separate quadrants:

- low registration - high threshold for noticing sensory input
- sensory sensitivity - low threshold for noticing sensory input
- sensation seeking - tendency to seek out sensory input
- sensation avoiding - tendency to avoid sensory input.

The sensory profile is conducted by an occupational therapist in collaboration with the individual. From analysis of the results, the occupational therapist is able to provide a clinical formulation regarding a person's unique sensory processing patterns, and provide insights regarding how these patterns may influence, enhance or interfere with daily functioning.

Taking into account the individual's unique sensory needs and preferences, the occupational therapist then coaches them to identify tailored coping strategies to improve wellbeing and enhance occupational performance.

While sensory profiles are not necessary for sensory modulation, some clinicians use it to better understand an individual's sensory sensitivities and thresholds prior to offering sensory modulation equipment. Sensory profiles can also be useful to identify differences in sensory patterns in families and groups. This can promote awareness and insight into how sensory modulation can improve interpersonal interactions and everyday functioning. When used to answer a specific clinical question or provide greater insight into an area of functioning, the sensory profile can illicit useful information and support specific recommendations.

Sensory discrimination

Sensory discrimination is the ability to differentiate between closely related sensory stimuli. It allows a person to recognise the subtle details of sensory inputs as well as between different sensations. An easy way to understand this is to think of examples from the senses:

- **proprioception:** how tightly does an egg have to be grasped without breaking it?
- **visual:** being able to look through the leaves and branches to see the bird in the tree
- **tactile:** being able to pick out the correct change in a pocket without looking
- **auditory:** being able to hear whether a person is saying fit, fat or foot?
- **taste:** can different flavours be tasted in the casserole?
- **smell:** is something burning?
- **interoception:** being able to identify whether feeling sick in the stomach or hungry?

(Bialer & Miller, 2011)

Sensory approaches

> *An umbrella term describing a range of models, assessments, interventions and tools involving the senses and sensory input, that support a person's ability to self regulate in more adaptive and effective ways. In doing so, an individual can be assisted to learn skills to better process sensory input, manage emotions, and improve daily functioning and quality of life. (Fitzgibbon and O'Sullivan, 2015)*
>
> *There are a variety of different sensory approaches that can be used to improve health and enhance functioning, including sensory assessments, modifying environments, and sensory items (such as fidget items) sensory modalities (including weighted items), sensory diets, and general sensory modulation techniques. (Champagne, 2008)*

Sensory items

Items or activities that reflect a person's unique sensory preferences and support their ability to positively change how they feel.

(Fitzgibbon and O'Sullivan, 2014)

Sensory items can assist a person to calm, soothe, activate, ground or focus. Examples of sensory items include stress balls, fidget items, hand-held massager, heat or cold pack, flavoured lollies, chewing gum, warm wrap, textured fabrics, poster of a rainforest and a skipping rope. Sensory items can be an important component of crisis planning due to their effectiveness in the management of intense or distressing emotions. Therefore there is also value in incorporating them into daily living activities and routines.

Sensory modalities

> *Sensory informed equipment prescribed by an occupational therapist to support a person's ability to change how they feel and self regulate.(Fitzgibbon & O'Sullivan, 2014)*

Recommendations are based on the unique sensory patterns and preferences of the individual. Examples of sensory modalities include weighted items, rocking chair, swings, hammocks, spinners and compression items or garments.

Weighted items have been used in mental health primarily for the positive effect of deep pressure sensory input. Tina Champagne et al. (2008) completed a pilot project on the use of weighted blankets and vests in the adult mental health population and found them to be useful for clients in reducing anxiety, feeling nurtured and reducing tremors. If using weighted blankets and lap pads, it is important to seek input from an occupational therapist, who will ensure a standardised and safe approach is adopted to ensure the consideration and management of risks.

Sensory Environments

Physical environments can play a significant role in positively influencing occupational patterns and performance (Champagne, 2006). The identification and modification of environmental factors impacting on an individual's sensory system can go a long way to enhance daily functioning. In doing so, it is essential to consider the individual's unique sensory needs and preferences. While some people prefer lower levels of sensory input, others prefer higher levels and variety. There are also many other people who prefer something in between!

People who prefer lower levels of sensory input are likely to responds better to neutral colours, silent or low sound, subtle or minimal scents, limited clutter and familiar furnishings. People who prefer a variety or high intensity of sensory input tend to seek vibrant or intense colours and images, loud or intense sound (e.g. music) and a variety of textures and scents.

Relevant environments where modifications could be of value include:

- health environments: set up, space, noise, light and smell. There needs to be variety to accommodate differences between individuals.
- home environments: space, arrangement of furnishings and kitchen, living and dining areas, solitary or shared accommodation, and the sensory patterns of the people residing with each other.
- community environments: access to outdoor space, views, preferred locations and proximity to shops, services, work and leisure spaces.

Accessibility of nature and outdoor environments

Modification of environments can incorporate the development of sensory spaces, the availability or portability of sensory items, consideration of preferred materials, products, equipment, layout and arrangement of spaces, and consideration of sensory needs when building and refurbishing. For example, a mental health unit can be designed to have a variety of spaces that cater for diverse sensory preferences, enabling people to meet their sensory needs and support the development of self-management skills for a wider range of people.

Sensory spaces

A range of areas and environments that provide a variety of sensory input to help a person change how they feel and self regulate (O'Sullivan and Fitzgibbon, 2016)

Sensory spaces can be indoors or outdoors, large or small, dedicated or multipurpose. They can include the necessary sensory input required to support a therapeutic outcome, or may need to be modified to contain sufficient sensory input (thus require a level of planning and design). Sensory spaces may have the necessary sensory input brought into the space (be completely portable) or items may need to be taken away or simplified (for example, removing clutter and eliminating odours).

It is important to be able to conceptualise a sensory space as being much more than just a room. A room, while a great resource for a service or individual fortunate enough to have access to it, can be limiting and run the risk of reducing accessibility. For example, if the sensory room is not able to be accessed or if there are not enough clinicians available to supervise its use, then the development of a sensory room is not a viable or practical option. It is really important to understand that sensory informed practice can occur in any situation and environment, not just in a dedicated room.

Examples of sensory spaces can include:

- sensory garden, nature space, water feature
- sensory corner, cabinet or wall
- purposeful sensory spaces or zones: quiet zone, music zone, movement zone
- modified home area: lounge, corner of bedroom, bathroom, and kitchen window sill
- looking at night sky from a window or backyard
- sensational space: one with lots of sensory modulation options. (quiet zone, active zone, loud zone, nature zone)

Sensory triggers

Sensory triggers are noxious sensations that can cause flashbacks, create anxiety or are aversive to the individual. Common sensations that can act as sensory triggers in some individuals include fingernails down a blackboard, sirens, flashing lights, loud or high pitched noises, light touch, whispering or particular smells associated with traumatic events (perfumes, deodorants, tobacco, grass or other odours). People with a trauma history may be unaware of certain sensory triggers that may cause such responses, and therefore can benefit from careful exploration of the senses to identify their personal sensory triggers. After engaging in this exploration, the individual can be supported to explore a variety of therapeutic interventions to assist with managing sensory triggers. Identification of sensory triggers can be incorporated into a Personal Safety Plan for use in an inpatient mental health unit.

Personal safety plan

A Personal Safety Plan (or Safety Tool) is a document that highlights individualised, sensory informed strategies useful during a crisis. The plan supports the person to identify and record sensations and experiences perceived as unpleasant and negative, and outlines practical strategies to help manage dysregulation and prevent escalation (Chalmers et al., 2012). A Personal Safety Plan must be completed by the individual, with assistance from a support person or health professional if required.

A study evaluated the implementation of basic sensory items and the use of a Safety Plan on an adult mental health inpatient unit (Lee, Cox, Whitecross, Williams & Hollander, 2010). Outcomes demonstrated significant reduction in the use of seclusion and restraint, as well as improved consumer perception of treatment.

Resources

For an example of a Personal Safety Plan, refer to:

- Chapter 16 Personal Safety Plan- Metro North Mental Health Service, Queensland, Australia.

Sensory kit

A collection of individualised sensory informed tools, activities and techniques that can be used 'in situ' to help a person positively change their feelings. Sensory kits can be used to help a person feel more grounded and connected, to calm and soothe, to manage cravings, to feel more energised or to improve concentration and focus.

Sensory items pertain to the person's unique sensory system and to the desired outcome, such as items to help manage anxiety, feel more grounded, manage anger, and deal with cravings. A sensory kit can be made from items around the home, without buying anything new.

Examples of a sensory kit include:

- a tub of items kept at home
- a portable pencil case that can fit into a handbag or backpack
- a list of suggested sensory activities, pictures, songs
- Prompts stored or apps downloaded on a smart phone.

Examples of sensory items that a person may include in a sensory kit are:

- chewing gum
- stress ball or fidget item
- stretchy bands
- scented candle
- flavoured tea bags
- nature items: leaves, shells, stone, wood
- sheepskin or soft pile cloth
- picture of the ocean, mountain, forest, beach
- adult colouring activity, doodle or puzzle books
- cue cards with reminders re deep breathing or stretches.

Resources

For more information on Sensory Kits, refer to:

- Chapter 16Factsheet on Sensory Kit
- *Sensory Kit examples on sensory modulation Pinterest*https://au.pinterest.com/SensoryMod/

Sensory diet

Developed in collaboration with an occupational therapist, a sensory diet is a range of sensory strategies used throughout the day to help manage everyday stresses and demands. By incorporating the techniques into their daily routine, the person is better able to meet their unique sensory needs, and maintain an optimal level of sensory input which promotes self organisation and enhances occupational performance.

Developing a sensory diet involves adding sensory informed activities into a person's routine, or better matching the sensory input to the individual in existing daily routines.

Examples of better matching the sensory input in existing daily routines:

- using citrus body wash in morning shower to wake up
- eating crunchy cereal at breakfast time to alert
- listening to IPod music on the bus
- sipping cold water and chewing carrot sticks in lectures to maintain focus
- going outside during lunchbreak to get some natural sunlight and walk around.

Examples of adding sensory informed activities into a person's routine:

- going for a daily walk
- reading a book or listening to music before bed
- using muscle-stretching activities or yoga poses throughout the day.

Resources

For more information on Sensory Diet, refer to:

- Chapter 16 Factsheet on Sensory Diet

Co-regulation

Co-regulation is when two or more people regulate their mood at the same time. This could include two people calming down by doing an activity together, or a crowd getting excited at a music concert! It is useful to keep in mind that if one person changes their mood, whether it be for the better or worse, this will have an impact on the other person too.

The process of co-regulation can be utilised in a thoughtful and constructive way by suggesting that an individual does sensory modulation activities with another person. Examples of positive co-regulation activities include:

- a couple lying on a hammock together
- a mother and son going for a walk along the river together
- a father pushing a child on a swing
- talking to a friend in a calm, soothing voice when they are feeling upset.

Chapter 16:

Factsheets and Worksheets

The resources and worksheets are also available in PDF at http://sensory-modulation-brisbane.com/

Password: ChangeHowYouFeel

Understanding sensory modulation.

Sensory modulation is 'changing how you feel through using your senses'. The senses include touch, movement taste, smell, sight and sound. Depending on the type of sensory input and our unique preferences, sensory modulation can increases feelings of calm, energy, improve focus and enhance feelings of safety and connection.

Sensations that involve deep touch and body and mouth movements are sometimes referred to as the power sensations because they can very rapidly effect positive change, especially for increasing feelings of safety and connection to others. However, as we are all different, people may find a range of sensory input works just as effectively.

How does it work?

Sensory modulation directly effects the autonomic nervous system (the fight or flight system) to quickly alter stress and arousal levels. Because the body and emotions (rather than our thinking) are used to change how we feel, sensory modulation is sometimes referred to as a type of **bottom up processing**.

Change is quick and effective because it:

1) targets lower rather than higher centres of the brain

2) does not try to change thinking to change feelings in the moment.

Benefits of sensory modulation

Sensory modulation is effective because it:

- can change stress levels by either calming or activating the nervous system
- works quickly and when it is needed
- works at the times when feeling distressed and overwhelmed
- helps to feel better without engaging thinking mechanisms
- helps build on skills to manage difficult situations and cope better
- helps build confidence and feelings of control in situations that have previously been avoided or worried about
- can promote participation in meaningful activities.

What is a sensory kit?

A sensory kit is a selection of sensory items that are easy to use and to access, which will help to increase positive feelings, improve mood, and reduce stress levels.

It is important that the items are inexpensive, easy to use, and meet a person's unique sensory needs. For example, a sensory kit to help someone feel more relaxed could include

- chewing gum or chewy lollies
- flavoured tea bags
- mini sketch or colouring book
- picture of favourite place (the beach, back garden)
- stress ball, mini rubix cube, something to fidget with
- reminder card with sensory activities written on it (i.e.- breathing, stretching)
- a reminder of a safe person (boyfriend deodorant) or a safe place (rosemary from the garden)

Sensory kit items can be kept in a box, case or a draw in the home. A sensory kit can be portable (to fit into a back pack or handbag) to help when a person is out and about.

Sensory reminders like music or pictures can be place on a smart phone or tablet to help prompt the use of sensory strategies.

What sort of sensory kit would be helpful?

e.g. - for sleep, cigarette cravings, anxiety on the bus, to feel connected to self, to focus

What are some sensory items to include in a sensory kit?

(think about the different senses: touch, taste, sight, sound, smell, movement)

What is a sensory diet?

A sensory diet is a range of sensory strategies and activities used throughout the day to help maintain positive feelings and a sense of wellbeing.

When built into daily routines, a sensory diet can support a person to use just the right amount of sensory input especially suited to their individual needs and preferences.

This helps us to meet the demands of the day, manage or lessen stress and feel more calm and in control.

Developing a sensory diet doesn't necessarily mean adding all new activities into a daily routine. In many cases it might be just making sure the activities already engaged in are tailored to better suit a person's sensory needs.

For example:

- listening to music you find relaxing at the end of the day or before you go to sleep
- choosing preferred fragrances for household cleaning products (citrus, lavender)
- eating crunchy cereals and sipping a hot cup of tea in the morning to help wake up
- going for a walk outside or doing some stretches throughout the day to maintain focus
- lying in a swing chair or hammock after work

Think about your usual daily routines and identify some sensory strategies that could help.

Routine activity	*Sensory modulation strategies to include in the activity*

My Sensory Goals

Senses	*Strategies for my Sensory Kit*	*Strategies for my day to day routines (Sensory Diet)*
Taste and oral motor		
Touch		
Deep pressure		
Movement		
Sight		
Sound		
Smell		

Taste and oral motor preferences

TASTES	*Like*	*Dislike*	*Impact on me calming/alerting/ grounding*
Sweet: fruit, vanilla, chocolate, honey, caramel, ice cream, ice blocks, pumpkin			
Spicy: chilli, herbs, cinnamon, pepper, thai food, curry, garlic, ginger, mint			
Salty: potato chips, pretzels, nuts, miso soup, vegemite, pickles			
Sour/ tart: lemon, lime, orange, sour lollies, sherbet, yoghurt, warheads			
Other: coffee, flavoured/herbal teas, slushy drinks, liquorish, gum mystery flavours			
Crunchy: raw vegetable sticks, apple, crackers, corn chips, popping candy, ice			
Chewy: gum, fruit chews, caramels, mentos, pop corn, al dente pasta			
Other: sucking through a straw, lollypop, blowing bubbles, whistling			

Touch, deep pressure and movement preferences

TOUCH	*Like*	*Dislike*	*Impact on me calming/ alerting/ grounding*
warm shower, ice pack, splash face, velvet, patting a pet, brushing hair, scarf, wheat pack , drawing, doodling, fidgeting			
DEEP PRESSURE/ PROPRIOCEPTION			
massage, vibration, clay work, blanket on lap, stretchy wrap, firm clothing, heavy work, gardening, wet towel on shoulders			
MOVEMENT			
spinning, swinging, rocking, stretching, tai chi, walking, cycling, gym, skipping, dancing			

Sight and sound preferences

SIGHT	*Like*	*Dislike*	*Impact on me calming/alerting/ grounding*
Nature: landscapes, beach, fields, mountains, gardens, flowers, animals			
Colours: bright, muted, dark, natural, patterns, neutral, lava lamp, glitter, sparkle			
Other: light levels, busy vs sparse, paintings, sculptures, magazines, books, photos (loved ones), sport			
SOUND			
Music: classical, jazz, pop, heavy metal, rock, country, spiritual, folk, gangster rap, trance, Bollywood, relaxation			
Natures sounds: rain, birds, waterfall, forest, ocean waves, wind, thunder, rain			
Other: traffic, white noise, talkback radio, crowds, whispers, sudden noises			

Smell preferences

SMELL	*Like*	*Dislike*	*Impact on me calming/alerting/ grounding*
Cooking: baked cookies or bread, ethnic foods (Italian, Asian, Indian), eggs, meat			
Food/drink: coffee, mint, basil, tuna, meat, coriander, vanilla, ginger, citrus, fruit, tea, alcohol			
Nature: roses, jasmine, lavender, cut grass, rain, hay, garden soil, eucalyptus			
Other: perfume, soap, body wash, essential oils, incense, household cleaning products, petrol, salt,			

Understanding how sensory modulation calms by thinking about what calms a baby

Strategy	Baby	Adolescent, Adult	How it works
Firm hug, wrapping	Firm hug Wrapping in blanket	Handbag or dog on lap Heavy doona Tight clothes	The firm pressure provides awareness of body in space (proprioception) and autonomic nervous system.
Rhythmic touch	Patting	Drumming Dancing	The rhythmic movement, sound and touch stimulates the vestibular, auditory and touch receptors and autonomic nervous system
Sucking	Sucking, eating	Sucking, eating	Sucking stimulates the facial muscles that regulate the limbic system Fosha, Siegel, & Solomon,(2009).
Sound	Lullaby Familiar voice Familiar sounds Singing Music	Familiar voice Familiar sounds Singing Music	Familiar voice provides a sense of safety. Music stimulates the auditory receptors and autonomic nervous system The heartbeat and breathing becomes 'entrained' to the rhythm.
Scent	Parents scent on cloth	Boyfriend's deodorant, mum's t-shirt or perfume	Olfactory input has a very quick pathway to the brain and is strongly linked with memory. Reminder of a loved one may assist us to feel safe.

Rating scale:

When asking a person to consider if a sensory modulation strategy will work for them, first identify the goal, then develop ratings accordingly.

Goal:

Doesn't work.......neutral........possibly works.......works a bit....... works a lot

Examples:

Goal: to calm:

calms a lot......calms a bit...... don't know......doesn't calm...... makes me worse

Goal: to feel more awake:

wakes me a lot.......wakes me a bit.......neutral.......doesn't wake me.......makes me worse

Goal: to feel grounded:

grounds me a lot.......grounds me a bit.......neutral.......doesn't ground me.......makes me worse

Self soothing

Soothing can be thought of as having 3 levels to it. Try to build up to the third level through practice:

Level 1: Soothe and relax your body and mind

***Level 2*:** Have the intention to soothe and nurture yourself

Level 3: Mindfully soothe and nurture yourself

Soothing things to look at:

Soothing things to listen to:

Soothing things to smell:

Soothing things to taste:

Soothing things to touch:

Soothing rocking or swinging movements:

Soothing heavy sensations, deep pressure, weight:

Soothing movement:

Soothing vibration:

Soothing temperature:

Other:

Self-soothing with movement, vibration and touch

Movement

- ☐ swing on a swing at a playground
- ☐ go for a drive with a friend
- ☐ rock in a rocking chair
- ☐ rock back and forth
- ☐ watch YouTube and do it e.g. tai chi
- ☐ walk along lines on the path
- ☐ sway to music
- ☐ crunch dry leaves
- ☐ dance slowly
- ☐ yoga or stretches
- ☐ ride on a ferry or other boat
- ☐ ride on a train
- ☐ balance on a log
- ☐ do the child's pose (yoga)
- ☐ float in a floatation tank
- ☐ float on the waves in the sea
- ☐ swing in a hammock

Light and Deep Touch

- ☐ give yourself a hand massage
- ☐ lay a bag of rice on your lap
- ☐ wrap a blanket tightly around u
- ☐ stroke a baby blanket
- ☐ stroke a scarf
- ☐ use a boyfriend or girlfriend pillow
- ☐ wrap a wet towel around shoulders
- ☐ lie under your doona.
- ☐ sit near a fan
- ☐ touch fabrics that are soothing.
- ☐ hug a plush toy
- ☐ touch moss or running water
- ☐ put cushions inside a doona and snuggle
- ☐

Vibration

- ☐ sit on a massage chair with vibration
- ☐ use a hand held massager on hand
- ☐ vibrating toothbrush or pillow

Most soothing options:

Calming sensations

Feel tight pressure through fabric, weight, touch

Wrap, Shawl, blanket, clothing, weight, sleeping bag, roll in doona

Rocking sensation

Hammock, yoga, gym equipment, kayak, swing, chair, bike riding, swimming

Soothing sounds

music, relaxation recording, natural sounds

Soothing scents

scents that remind you of connection to others or nature

Other

pictures, images, tastes, chewing, activities

Sensory modulation to engage in occupations

This worksheet will assist you to think of the things that you want to do and the places to do them and how sensory modulation could assist you to do it.

What do you want to do?

e.g. work, study, cook, exercise, clean, play with kids, socialise, use computer, recreation, sleep

Where do you want to be able to do it?

e.g. home, office, park, bus, school, stadium, centre, hospital

What emotion or alertness level do you need to have to do this?

e.g. calm, alert, excited, sleepy

What sensory input may assist with this?

e.g. sensory input e.g. rock, spin, move, weight or stretch, touch, feel, see, listen, taste, smell

What sensory items may assist with this?

e.g. heat pack, ice pack, weighted cushion, warheads, earplugs, white noise, nilodour, photos, vanilla

What changes to the environment may assist with this?

e.g. dim lights, walk outside, move away from noise, change the work station, decrease the temperature

Alerting and focusing sensations for a meeting, school or lecture

Oral Motor:

chewy food, crunchy food, strong flavours, mints, hot drink, cold drink

Scent:

mint, lemongrass, rosemary, lemon

Touch:

press fingers hard, trace finger nails, blue tack, fidget items, pen with texture, item on keyring, sea shell, scarf, ring

Movement:

jiggle your leg, chair pushups, getting up and standing, changing posture

Visual:

doodling, taking notes, focusing on pictures in slides, looking at person intently

Changing substance use with sensory modulation

Oral motor: do I like what the substance does in my mouth?
e.g. chewing, blowing, sucking, sipping, cool or hot in mouth

Sensory modulation oral motor strategies include:
chewy food, crunchy food, strong flavours, mints, hot drink, cold drink, food

Other:

Scent: do I like what the substance does in my nose or the scent?
e.g. sniffing, inhaling, hot or cold temperature, scent of ....

Sensory modulation nose or scent strategies include:
inhaling steam, hot herbal drinks, vick's inhaler, tigerbalm cream, scent: mint, lemongrass, rosemary, lemon

Other:

Touch: do I like the touch of the substance? Or the changes to the sense of touch?
e.g. rolling a joint, holding a glass, piercing of skin, relaxed muscles, tense muscles, flushing, coolness, hypersensitivity

Sensory modulation touch strategies include:
rolling a fidget toy, shelling nuts, holding a non-alcoholic drink, warm hot towel, warm bath, different textured fabrics, cold shower, fidget items, hand-held massager

Other:

Movement: do I like the movement sensations?
e.g. dizziness, spin, lack of co-ordination, more co-ordination?

Sensory modulation movement strategies include:
spinning around on a chair, dancing, circus, gym equipment

Other:

Visual: do I like the visual sensations?
e.g. brighter, blurry, more intense, sharper?

Sensory modulation movement strategies include:
YouTube videos, kaleidoscopes, art, lava lamps

Other:

Intense sensations

Movement

- ☐ Suck on a lemon
- ☐ Spin around and around until dizzy
- ☐ Suck a strong mint or warhead
- ☐ Gargle intense mouthwash
- ☐ Have a cold or hot shower
- ☐ Suck on an ice cube
- ☐ Clap your hands together hard
- ☐ Listen to loud music
- ☐ Suck on a piece of raw ginger
- ☐ Try a new fruit
- ☐ Eat a hard lolly or toffee
- ☐ Skip with a rope until exhausted
- ☐ Ask for a tight hug
- ☐ Eat a curry
- ☐ Smell smelling salts or peppermint
- ☐ Apply a heavy facial e.g. mud
- ☐ Blow up a balloon until it pops
- ☐ Rub your hands together until hot

Light and Deep Touch

- ☐ Chew a sour lolly
- ☐ Rub dencorub or tigerbalm on your arm
- ☐ Lay a 5kg bag of rice on your lap
- ☐ Bite into a chilli. Taste salt flakes
- ☐ Hold your breath as long as you can.
- ☐ Spin on a roundabout
- ☐ Bite into a clove of garlic
- ☐ Hold a strong yoga stretch
- ☐ Spin on an office chair till dizzy
- ☐ Listen to loud white noise
- ☐ Swing high on a kids swing
- ☐ Do push-ups or star jumps till exhausted
- ☐ Intense food or drink
- ☐ Stare at a candle flame for a long time
- ☐ Dye hair with henna
- ☐ Go cross eyed for as long as you can
- ☐ Smell aniseed, eucalyptus oil or tea tree oil
- ☐ Wax your legs

Intense sensations to try:

Identifying sensory factors to feeling on edge or upset

Questions to ask self when unsure why you are upset, and you think it may be the environment.

Is it the smell?

Is it the sounds?

Is it the brightness or flashing of lights?

Is it the low levels of light and darkness?

Is it the height?

Are lots of things moving past me quickly?

Is it the movement?

Are people bumping into me?

Is it hard to walk? E.g. uneven surfaces?

Does this remind me of something?

What am I thinking?

Personal safety plan

Queensland Government Royal Brisbane & Women's Hospital Metro North Mental Health RBWH **PERSONAL SAFETY PLAN**	(Affix patient identification label here) URN: Family Name: Given Names: Address: Date of Birth: Sex: ☐ M ☐ F ☐ I

This **PERSONAL SAFETY PLAN** helps to identify ways for you to calm emotions and manage stressful situations by increasing understanding of:

- Your early warning signs and triggers of stress and upset;
- Your unique sensory preferences and sensory based activities which are helpful for coping.

Warning Signs: What are some of the things that indicate that I am becoming angry or upset?

☐ Crying	☐ Speaking loudly or rudely	☐ Shortness of breath
☐ Racing thoughts	☐ Rocking	☐ Swearing
☐ Shaking	☐ Sweating	☐ Pointing finger / waving arms
☐ Inability to sit still	☐ Clenching fists or teeth	☐ Racing heart
☐ Isolating myself	☐ Wringing hands	☐ Bouncing legs
☐ Pacing/ walking	☐ Headache or tension in other parts of my body	☐ Having bad thoughts about myself or others
☐ Butterflies or sick feeling in stomach	☐ Acting out of character *(please explain)*	☐ Other *(please list)* ....

Triggers: What are some of the things that can trigger me to feel upset?

☐ Cravings (What?)	☐ Wearing hospital gowns (Please explain)
☐ Reminders/ memories of the past (What?)	☐ Not feeling safe (Please explain)
☐ People doing or saying certain things (Please explain)	☐ Distressing thoughts or nightmares (Please explain)
☐ Particular times of the day (When?)	☐ Ward routines (Please explain) ....
☐ Particular times of the year (When?)	☐ Not having control or input (Please explain) ....
☐ Contact with particular people (Who?)	☐ Other: (Please describe) ....

USING OUR SENSES TO CALM AND SOOTHE

Visual preferences: What I like, really dislike, & what is useful to calm me

	Like	Really dislike	Useful to calm me		Like	Really dislike	Useful to calm me
Bright / intense light	☐	☐	☐	Open curtain	☐	☐	☐
Natural light	☐	☐	☐	Closed curtain	☐	☐	☐
Dim light / darker	☐	☐	☐	Watch a movie / tv	☐	☐	☐
Bare walls (no clutter)	☐	☐	☐	Reading	☐	☐	☐
Familiar items	☐	☐	☐	Art and craft	☐	☐	☐
Busy environment / people around	☐	☐	☐	Puzzles, card games	☐	☐	☐

PERSONAL SAFETY PLAN

DO NOT WRITE IN THIS BINDING MARGIN

MR OPD 195
V5.00 - 02/2014
Locally printed
00201:00195

Queensland Government

Royal Brisbane & Women's Hospital

Metro North Mental Health RBWH

PERSONAL SAFETY PLAN

(Affix patient identification label here)

URN:

Family Name:

Given Names:

Address:

Date of Birth: Sex: ☐ M ☐ F ☐ I

Sound preferences: What I like, really dislike, & what is useful to calm me

	Like	Really dislike	Useful to calm me		Like	Really dislike	Useful to calm me
Loud / sudden noise	☐	☐	☐	Playing instruments	☐	☐	☐
High pitched noise	☐	☐	☐	Ear plugs	☐	☐	☐
Whispering	☐	☐	☐	Guided relaxation	☐	☐	☐
Silence	☐	☐	☐	Nature sounds	☐	☐	☐
Background noise / white noise	☐	☐	☐	Listening to music	☐	☐	☐

Touch and body preferences: What I like, really dislike, & what is useful to calm me

	Like	Really dislike	Useful to calm me		Like	Really dislike	Useful to calm me
Temperature – Cool or warm	☐	☐	☐	Fidget item or stress ball	☐	☐	☐
Cold or hot shower	☐	☐	☐	Lying on bed	☐	☐	☐
Wrapped in blanket	☐	☐	☐	Ice pack/ cool wash cloth	☐	☐	☐
Brush/ style my hair	☐	☐	☐	Being by myself	☐	☐	☐
Going for a walk	☐	☐	☐	Deep breathing	☐	☐	☐
Pacing	☐	☐	☐	Hugging a pillow	☐	☐	☐
Human touch	☐	☐	☐	Distraction	☐	☐	☐
Writing/ doodling	☐	☐	☐	Injection	☐	☐	☐
Massage	☐	☐	☐	Group activities	☐	☐	☐
Exercising	☐	☐	☐	Gentle stretching	☐	☐	☐

Taste and smell: What I like, really dislike, & what is useful to calm me

	Like	Really dislike	Useful to calm me		Like	Really dislike	Useful to calm me
Hot or cold drink	☐	☐	☐	Other foods	☐	☐	☐
Ice/ slushy drink	☐	☐	☐	Certain drinks	☐	☐	☐
Sucking on a straw	☐	☐	☐	Certain smells	☐	☐	☐
Chewing gum	☐	☐	☐	Body odour	☐	☐	☐
Sour lollies	☐	☐	☐	Body wash	☐	☐	☐
Crunchy food	☐	☐	☐	Certain soaps	☐	☐	☐
Bland food	☐	☐	☐	Medication	☐	☐	☐

Other things that may be helpful, or things that a family member or friend could do or bring to help me feel calm: ....

....

....

Has this raised any issues that you would like to discuss further?

....

....

Consumer Signature: .... Date: ...... / ...... / ......

Staff member to sign if assisting or discussing with consumer:

Name: .... Designation: .... Signature: .... Date: ...... / ...... / ......

DO NOT WRITE IN THIS BINDING MARGIN

Page 2 of 2

Personal Safety Plan (worksheet), (2013) Metro North Hospital and Health Service, used with permission

Chapter 17:

Leisure, Interests, Sport Through the Senses (LISTS)

Leisure, Interests, Sports Through the Senses

(LISTS)

LISTS is also available in PDF at http://sensory-modulation-brisbane.com/

Password: ChangeHowYouFeel

Information:

LISTS are divided into sections based on your senses. This includes sound, sight, taste, smell, touch and your body feeling relaxed, pressure, movement or thrilled.

If you seek or avoid particular senses then you could select a list based on those preferences.

If you prefer primarily indoor or primarily outdoor interests, then select those lists.

The last pages assist you to identify what might assist you to start or join in on your interests.

Hopefully you will find something that sparks your interest.

Sections include:

Visual, observation, watching

Music, quiet or loud sounds

Texture, touch, doing things with your hands

Relaxing, focused or meditative activities

Heavy work, deep pressure

Movement or sports

Thrill seeking

Taste and smell

Messy, getting your hands dirty

What may help you to join in?

Leisure, Interests, Sports Through the Senses (LISTS)

Visual Outdoors	*Experienced this*	*Interested in this*
photography		
train spotting		
bird watching		
walking		
reading		
book clubs		
gardening		
geocaching		
outdoor art		
yarn bombing		
cloud spotting		
snorkeling		
insect identification		
coin, bottles		
sculpture		
kites		
astronomy		
watching sport		
fossicking		
whale watching		
historical sites		
construction viewing		
people watching		
window shopping		
snorkeling		
remote control cars or boats		

Leisure, Interests, Sports Through the Senses (LISTS)

Visual Indoors	*Experienced this*	*Interested in this*
puzzles, mazes		
magazines, comics		
movies at home		
movies at cinema		
mahjong, cards		
Scrapbooking, decoupage		
crosswords, sudoku		
lead lighting		
stamp collecting		
model trains		
drawing, art		
writing, poetry		
computer games		
card games		
reading		
art galleries		
model planes		
origami		
where's wally books		
aquariums, fish, sea monkeys		
antiques		
lego, mecanno		
computers, social media, websites		
photography		
board games		
jewelry		
sewing, quilting		

Leisure, Interests, Sports Through the Senses (LISTS)

Relaxing, Meditative, Indoors	*Experienced this*	*Interested in this*
yoga		
meditation		
qui gong, tai chi		
pilates		
exercises, eg pushups		
gym equipment		
music, dancing		
taekwondo		
knitting		
fitness DVDs		
hula hoops		
aerobics		

Relaxing, Meditative, Outdoors	*Experienced this*	*Interested in this*
walking		
gardening		
yoga, pilates		
exercise in the park		
jogging, running		
meditation		
skipping rope		
circus e.g. trapeze, fire twirling		
tai chi, qi gong		
swimming, surfing		

Leisure, Interests, Sports Through the Senses (LISTS)

Movement Outdoors - by your self	*Experienced this*	*Interested in this*
cycling, BMX bikes		
skipping rope		
golf		
exercises in the park		
bouldering, parkour		
roller skating, blading		
weights		
running, jogging		
archery		
canoeing, kayak		
swim, dive		
dancing with dogs		
four wheel driving		

Movement Outdoors - with others	*Experienced this*	*Interested in this*
trapeze, slack rope		
beach volleyball, ultimate frisbee		
basketball, netball, water polo		
badminton, tennis		
jousting		
cricket, hockey		
touch football, soccer, rugby		
quiddich		
lawn bowls, bocce		

Leisure, Interests, Sports Through the Senses (LISTS)

Movement Indoors - by your self	***Experienced this***	***Interested in this***
wii		
skipping rope		
yoga, pilates		
exercises, e.g. pushups		
zumba, gym		
juggling		
darts		
hula hoops		
basketball		
weights, treadmill		

Movement Indoors - with others	***Experienced this***	***Interested in this***
indoor rock climbing		
gymnastics, circus		
ice hockey		
ice skating, roller skating		
ten pin bowling		
indoor volleyball, netball		
playing pool, snooker		
fencing		
handball		
dancing		
judo		
squash		

Leisure, Interests, Sports Through the Senses (LISTS)

Sound Indoors	*Experienced this*	*Interested in this*
playing musical instrument		
playing recorded music or radio		
computer games		
choir, band, singing, chanting		
model cars		
playing with children		
hanging out with friends		
dancing		
audio books		
bingo		
leatherwork		
rock tumbling		
absolute silence		
book clubs		
TV, DVDs		
speed dating		
zumba		
poetry and story telling		
hip hop dance		
bollywood dance		
flamenco dance		
latin dance		
tap dance		
ballroom dance		
break dance		
line dancing		
ballet		

Leisure, Interests, Sports Through the Senses (LISTS)

Sound Outdoors	*Experienced this*	*Interested in this*
outdoor bands, choirs		
plane, train spotting		
dance		
watching sport		
bird spotting		
bush walking		
using gardening tools, e.g. mowing, chainsaw		
using cleaning tools e.g. blower vac		
visiting dog parks		
Woodworking, building		
metal work		
hot rods and vintage		
yodeling		
frog spotting		
speed dating		
speedway		
go carts		
boating		
surfing		
poetry performances		
festivals		
horse riding		
roller coasters. fun parks		
capoeira (dance/martial art)		
medieval cannons		
animal care		

Leisure, Interests, Sports Through the Senses (LISTS)

Thrill seeking	*Experienced this*	*Interested in this*
fire twirling		
bungee jumping		
roller coasters, fun park rides		
skateboards		
rock climbing		
mountain biking		
jet skiing		
car racing, motor biking		
canyoning		
scuba diving		
abseiling		
spear fishing		
skiing, snowboarding		
scary movies		
speedway		
diving		
spelunking (caves)		
making rockets		
skydiving		
hang gliding, parachuting		
white water rafting		
tobogganing		
sailing		
jousting		
skirmish		
zorbing		
tightrope, slackrope, trapeze		

Leisure, Interests, Sports Through the Senses (LISTS)

Taste and Smell Indoors	*Experienced this*	*Interested in this*
cooking		
baking bread		
indoor garden e.g. herbs		
scent jars, monclin, vials,		
oil burners		
candle making		
soap making		
perfume making		
aromatic baths		
brewing beer		
cooking curries		
crafts e.g. pot pourri, lavender bags		
massage with oils		
church, mosque, temple		
batik		

Leisure, Interests, Sports Through the Senses (LISTS)

Taste and Smell Outdoors	*Experienced this*	*Interested in this*
eating out		
wine tasting		
mindful tasting or smelling		
swimming in pools or ocean		
visiting scented gardens		
community gardens		
gardening		
smells of nature		
herb society		
oil painting		
pressing flowers		
cheese tasting		
growing herbs		
smelling flowers		
shopping for body products or perfume		

Leisure, Interests, Sports Through the Senses (LISTS)

Texture and Touch Outdoors	*Experienced this*	*Interested in this*
weaving		
basket making		
knitting		
poetry		
macramé		
sewing		
building		
caring for pets		
yarn bombing		
caring for wildlife e.g. injured		
carving		
bark art		
curbside collection fossicking		
sandcastle, stone sculptures		
mud bricks, pizza ovens		

Leisure, Interests, Sports Through the Senses (LISTS)

Texture and Touch Indoors	*Experienced this*	*Interested in this*
paper making		
felting		
knitting, crochet		
animation, clay		
macramé		
sewing		
quilting		
restoring furniture		
jewelry making		
origami		
lead light		
embroidery		
weaving		
pottery, ceramics		
bread making		

Leisure, Interests, Sports Through the Senses (LISTS)

Messy - getting your hands dirty	*Experienced this*	*Interested in this*
clay		
gardening		
bush regeneration		
bread making		
mud wrestling		
ceramics		
sculpture e.g. sand, stone		
building, woodwork		
baking		
painting		
batik		
mechanics		
mosaics		
leatherwork		
camp fires		
caring for animals		

Leisure, Interests, Sports Through the Senses (LISTS)

Heavy work, deep pressure	**Experienced this**	**Interested in this**
wakeboarding		
rock climbing		
gardening		
rugby		
weight lifting		
kick boxing, judo		
medieval tournaments		
jousting		
digging for bottles, coins		
bouldering		
metal detecting		
team sports		
roller derby		
fencing		
gymnastics		
wood chopping (including comps)		

My top activities, sports or leisure ideas are:

To ***participate in the leisure, Interest and Sports I would need to:***

☐	have/save more money
☐	increase confidence being around other people
☐	be confident with catching public transport
☐	be confident with driving
☐	have someone to go with
☐	have the equipment or know where to get it
☐	feel happier or more motivated
☐	be confident with talking with other people
☐	keep the noise levels down
☐	be less paranoid
☐	know that it was on the right time of day e.g. early morning, late afternoon, night
☐	know where the toilets are
☐	know there are people similar to me. (what sort of similarity)
☐	find the time
☐	understand the activity e.g. the rules of the game
☐	tolerate the feeling of the uniform
☐	lose weight
☐	reduce drug or alcohol use
☐	Have the kids looked after

Notes:

Chapter 18:

Risk Management Information

Risk Management information

Risks checklist

Monitoring a person's use of sensory items is important to ensure appropriate and safe use. The level of supervision necessary will depend on the type of item being used, the consumer themselves and the environment in which they are being used.

Specific equipment

Weighted modalities	**Weighted blankets, lap pads, shoulder wraps, vests**
Suffocation	Person must be able to remove item independently. Sedation and Intoxication would impair ability to remove
Thermoregulation	Consider if modifying air temperature or size of modality can minimise risk of over -heating
Weight ratio	Ratio of weighted item to weight of consumer: no more than 10% Ration of weighted item to weight of staff: no more than 10%
Skin integrity	Weight should not be applied over injury or skin lesion unless medically cleared. Consider integrity of frail skin
Existing medical Conditions	Prior medical clearance for people with heart & pulmonary conditions, pregnancy, post-surgery, eating disorders etc.
Intentional misuse	Supervision protocols and clear guidelines for use required. Seek agreement from client regarding correct use of modality
Trips risk	Proper storage of items Consideration of size of & locations for use of items
Proximity to others	Consider location for use of items Ensure a weighted modality plan is completed for each person
Alternatives to weighted blankets	Rice sack in pillow case or cushion, back pack with books, gym weights, mascots, stretchy wraps, plastic bottles filled with water, cans of food, weight bearing or heavy activities (digging in garden, sweeping, cleaning windows, watering garden with buckets)
Rocking/moving Equipment	**Rocking chair, glider, spinning stool, hammock, massage chair**
Blood pressure	Consider safe pace/intensity of activity Provide adequate monitoring/ supervision
Fitness	Start slow, gradual increase in pace & intensity if appropriate
Trip risk/ catching items of clothing	Consider appropriate clothing & supervision when using equipment

Jamming/ pinching fingers	Provision of education prior to use of equipment Provision of supervision as appropriate
Ability to use equipment	Getting into & out of chairs, falls risk, cognitive functioning Provision of appropriate education/ monitoring & support
Alternatives to rocking/ moving equipment	Exercise equipment in local parks, swings, slides, skipping, bouncing & catching a ball
Smell	
Can scent be controlled by the individual?	In environments like an inpatient unit, scent must be able to be controlled by the person (i.e.- type & intensity) as what is calming for one could be noxious/ triggering/allergic for another
Strong association with memory	Be aware of the connection with memory, especially could be triggering for those with a trauma background
Risk management	Discuss ways of managing triggers prior to intervention Explore response to different scents When exploring sensory items, work up to sense of smell
Sound	
Consider aspects of sound	Volume, pace, tempo, beat, rhythm, predictability What people find calming/ grounding could be quite different
Consider multiple sounds	More than one sound/layers may be overwhelming. When under stress, we are more sensitive to distal/ unpredictable noises (machinery, clattering trolleys, doors)
Ligature risk of headphone cords	Cordless/ wireless options
Could lyrics/song words be triggering?	Consider music without lyrics
Can sound by controlled by the individual?	In environments like an inpatient unit, helpful for sound to be controlled by the person (i.e. type & volume)
Touch	
Allergies	Latex, skin sensitivities Review alerts, check with person/ significant others
Infection control measures	Guidelines to clean sensory items after use Use of hand sanitiser prior to contact with items Universal precautions apply
Sight	
Light intensity	Ensure old/ flickering bulbs are replaced Access to natural light and moveable window shades Consider dimmer switches or florescent light to dampen intensity

Effects of blue light	Blue light on TV, PC & smart phone screens effect pineal gland & can interfere with sleep. There are apps to turn down blue light or orange lens glasses to assist with sleep. Exposure to natural during day can reduce impact of blue light on sleep.
View of nature	Access to/ view of/ pictures of natural settings (gardens, ocean, fish tank, mountains) has been shown to increase calm & grounding.
Taste	
Calorie intake	Consult with dietician if preferences are providing excessive calories
Food allergies/ preferences	Intolerances, severe allergies, diet choices (vegan, vegetarian) Review alerts/ check with person/ significant others
Oral motor difficulties	Difficulty chewing or swallowing, texture & taste sensitivities, dentures or dental issues.

Chapter 19:

Sensory Spaces Worksheets

Sensory space audit

The Sensory Space Audit can be completed through moving through the environment and stopping in different spots every few metres and documenting the present and potential sensory input there.

- What smells are present now? Any likely smells in the future (e.g. close to lunch or toilet)
- What sights? Lighting? Darkness?
- Are there any bright lights, fluorescent lights or flashing lights?
- Usual temperatures? Hot spots or cooler spots?
- What sounds are present now? What are likely sounds in the future?
- Is there an echo quality to the sound? (reverberation)
- What textures are present?
- Any water or other features that invite or repel touch experiences?
- Any risky features? Trip hazards?
- What is there that facilitates social connection?
- What is there that detracts from social connection?
- Any features that allow someone to spin, rock, sway or swing?
- Opportunities for movement
- Opportunities for rest and stillness
- How much privacy is there?
- Where do people walk through the area?

Designing or renovating sensational spaces in hospitals, mental health units and aged care facilities

Exercise zone or gym

- non slip mats on the floor with vinyl rectangular cushions sectioning off the area so it is not walked over
- ideally near a wall. On the wall could be posters with exercises that could assist with anger (e.g. wall pushups, simple yoga and stretches)
- equipment including weights, basketball hoops and an exercise ball to sit on or bounce.

Calm garden zone

- garden with variety of plants including variety of leaf shapes and textures
- scent to be carefully considered. Would not recommend strong scents in garden zone. Could have a separate zone with scented plants (scent exploration zone)
- good to have soothing quality to plants and zone
- water feature e.g. pond or waterfall or water sculpture
- no hidden or dark zones to assist with soothing (so can let go of hypervigilance).

Family interaction zone

- indoor or (ideally) outdoor area for parents and children
- swings or playground equipment that promotes interaction, connection and co-regulation
- sandpit or water play
- games table
- area for ball games.

Low stimulation zone

- eye masks
- ear plugs, noise-cancelling headphones, music and earphones
- wrap or blanket
- comfortable, rocking or swinging chair
- lower light, light with dimmer switch, low lamp
- white noise or soundproofing of zone
- nil odour (takes away the scent)
- no talking in zone.

Inspiring, creative zone

- inspiring art prints or pictures
- art materials, clay, beads, craft materials
- easels set up
- shelving with examples of things that can be made.

Music or auditory zone

- area for music therapy or musicians
- music playing
- musical instruments
- space for dancing
- sound proofing or acoustic tiles.
- chair with headphones embedded in it.

TV zone

- soundproofing so that noise of TV does not travel
- or headphones
- chairs spaced apart
- TV is set to the side so that people do not have to walk past and be potentially disturbed by the visual stimulation.

Eating zone

- space for those who would like to sit by self
- some social table arrangements
- choice of food tastes and textures
- management of acoustics through acoustic panels, chairs with felt bases, mats on floor (to minimise sound of scraping chairs
- consideration of strong smells (e.g. tuna) and ability to manage these.

Socialising zone

- area that is conducive to socialising
- chairs around tables. Flexible seating arrangements possible to enable small groups
- shelving with board games
- background music should be low or not used (to assist people who have trouble filtering background sound).

Soothing comfort zone

- comfortable lounge chair, bean bags, swinging chair, rocking chair, massage chair with soft or textured cushions and wraps
- weighted cushions or wraps
- velvet, valour, shag pile rug
- heated blankets
- personal mini massagers
- foot baths.

Pet or therapeutic animal zone

- aquarium with fish
- area designed to interact with chickens, guinea pigs, visiting dogs or cats etc.

Walking or pacing zone

- area designed for walking
- in dementia units, include paths that can be walked around in a circuitous fashion, without feeling that it is circular e.g. lots of plants, small safe water feature, winding flat path with handrails and clearly designated path
- provide visual interest (e.g. flower garden, sculpture, small safe water feature, bamboo garden, succulent's garden, chicken area with coup etc.
- width of the path should enable a couple of people to pass each other safely. Walking this path may be used for angry or agitated persons and they need to be given space
- designed to not cast many shadows or dark areas or suddenly moving items as this increases agitation and hypervigilance.

Scent exploration zone

- this area would ideally be outdoor as scent can be a trauma trigger for some people
- plants may include herbs, scented flowers and leaves (e.g. geraniums) and fruit e.g. strawberries
- small jars of scents including household and kitchen scents. These could be added to small individual pots for an individual kit.

Vegie patch

- promote digging or weeding to increase movement and proprioceptive input e.g. digging up sweet potatoes.

Reading zone

- comfortable chairs, cushions
- bookcase
- books, magazine, inspirational books, picture books, poetry, crossword or Sudoku books.

Icy zone

- low basin for icy water. For clients to place their head in and reduce anger or anxiety.
- small fridge with ice packs, icy balls, ice to suck, slushees. Also cold water in zip lock bags.
- water drainage on floor
- non slip mats
- marking around zone to suggest that someone in that zone may not wish to speak or interact.
- away from kids zone and noisy zones.

Game zone

- room set up for computer game use e.g. Wii, Nintendo
- headphones (wireless) may reduce noise levels.

Massage zone

- massage chair

- mini personal massagers
- massage table for visiting masseurs
- massage mat on chair
- hand and body creams
- foot baths.

Sensory modulation item zone

Sensory modulation items set up for individuals to access

- weighted cushions, wraps
- blankets, shawls
- textured cushions
- cardboard boxes to personalise a distress tolerance kit
- scented items
- icy spray
- fidget items
- books for sudoku or crosswords
- warheads, sour lollies, mints
- dencorub, eucalyptus rub.

Items are assessed and selected with the intention of clients using them independently, without needing a staff member to access or unlock them. For example, some inpatient units have a sensory modulation box beside each bed.

Designing or renovating sensational spaces in schools

Schools could become sensational spaces with zones that consider neurodiversity. At lunchtimes children benefit from being able to choose whether they need to move their bodies, reduce their sensory stimulation or engage in calming, soothing play. Classrooms could also be designed to have a sensory box, sensory modulation items or to become a sensory space.

Low stimulation zone:

In a school area, it would be preferable to have an indoor and an outdoor space that is low stimulation. For many schools, this is the library, however libraries are frequently providing iPad and computer games available in lunch times. These are not suitable for children needing low stimulation, a quiet space or a time out, due to the visual movement, bright lights and sounds.

Indoor low stimulation zone

- eye masks
- ear plugs, noise-cancelling headphones, music and earphones
- wrap or blanket
- comfortable chair, rocking chair, swinging chair, hammock, cushions
- lower light, dimmer switch, low lamp
- white noise or soundproofing of zone
- nil odour (takes away the scent)
- no talking in zone
- could use a box or tent with cushions (sensory retreat).

Outdoor low stimulation zone

- ear plugs, noise-cancelling headphones, music and earphones
- away from toilets, eating areas, scented gardens or other scented areas
- away from lots of visual movement (e.g. other kids running around, playground equipment)
- swings, hammocks, cacoon swing chairs
- could use a box or tent with cushions (sensory retreat).

High vestibular zone

- spinning equipment and toys e.g. spinners, roundabouts, bilibo
- rocking equipment, individual rockers, large rockers
- hopscotch on ground
- skipping ropes
- balancing equipment
- flying fox (if permitted).

Nature play area

- sand, dirt, water
- water tables, creeks, pvc pipes, watering cans

- wheelbarrows
- spades, buckets, sandcastle moulds
- leaves, rocks, sticks to play with.

Inspiring, creative zone

- art materials, clay, beads, craft materials
- easels set up
- play dough.

Playground

- climbing equipment
- balancing boards or stepping stones
- slides.

Oval

- area for children to run, play ball games etc.

Music or auditory zone:

- outdoor instruments, clapsticks, xylophones, drums
- space for dancing
- music.

Eating zone:

- acoustics managed to minimise reverberation of sounds of kids talking and eating
- space for those who would like to sit by self
- social table arrangements
- choice of food tastes and textures
- consideration of strong smells (e.g. tuna) and ability to manage these
- seating to be mindful of forming clique's or excluding other children (e.g. if there is a table and chair for four then a fifth person would be excluded unless they can pull up a chair).

Socialising zone

- area that is conducive to socialising
- chairs around tables. Flexible seating arrangements possible to enable small but inclusive groups
- shelving with board games.

Pet or therapeutic animal zone

- aquarium with fish
- area designed to interact with chickens, guinea pigs, other animals.

Vegie patch

- patches would ideally promote digging or weeding as this would increase movement and proprioceptive input e.g. digging up sweet potatoes.

Sensory modulation item zone

Sensory modulation items set up for individuals to access, either on shelves, within the space or in a calm kit.

- weighted cushions, wraps
- weighted knitted chickens, weighted plush or vinyl toys
- velcro with wool threaded through to fidget with
- blankets, shawls
- textured cushions, mermaid cushions
- play doh
- scented rubbers
- lava lamps or liquid
- bean bags
- bilibo
- balance board, wobble cushion
- ear defenders ear muffs, ear plugs
- nil odour to remove smell
- books
- fidget items
- kinetic sand.

Resources

- equipment list in chapter 14

Further ideas are available at the sensory modulation Pinterest account: https://it.pinterest.com/SensoryMod

Designing or renovating sensational spaces in community spaces

In a community space, café, shop, playground and public space, consideration of ways to be more inclusive of those with sensory sensitivities or to offer a place where a person can engage in sensory modulation activities, can help individuals feel more calm and more able to engage and participate in that environment.

Sensory modulation calm kit

Sensory modulation items set up for individuals to access, either on shelves, within the space or in a calm kit, for example

- ear plugs
- nil odour bottle
- noise-cancelling headphones, ear defenders, sonic defenders
- white noise machine
- virtual reality goggles
- hand grip strengthener
- instant ice or instant heat packs
- books, magazines, crosswords or Sudoku books
- signs that indicate there are freezer packs available for calming, electric hot water bottles, and that jumping up and down in the bathroom is welcome
- weighted cushion (or five kg bag of rice inside a cover)
- moh doh.

Calming zone

- massage mat for chair
- swing chair or hammock
- weighed cushions, throws, wraps, blankets
- space for someone to sit by self without needing to talk.
- space for someone to sit and engage with other people e.g. available for a board game, chat.

Soothing comfort zone

- comfortable lounge chair, bean bags, swinging chair, rocking chair, massage chair with soft or textured cushions and wraps
- weighted cushions or wraps
- velvet, valour, shag pile rug
- heated blankets
- personal mini massagers
- massage mat for chair
- space for someone to sit by self without needing to talk
- space for someone to sit and engage with other people e.g. available for a board game, chat.

Adult playgrounds

- gym equipment, signs with exercises on it
- swings for adults
- zip lines
- cacoons
- balancing boards, bosu balls.

Resources

- adult playground pictures are available at the sensory modulation Pinterest account: https://it.pinterest.com/SensoryMod/

Calm garden zone

- water feature e.g. pond or waterfall or water sculpture
- garden with variety of plants including variety of leaf shapes and textures
- scent to be carefully considered. Would not recommend strong scents in garden zone. Could have a separate zone with scented plants (scent exploration zone)
- good to have soothing quality to plants and zone.

Low stimulation zone

- eye masks
- ear plugs, noise-cancelling headphones, music and earphones
- wrap or blanket
- comfortable chair, rocking chair, swinging chair
- lower light, dimmer switch, low lamp
- white noise or soundproofing of zone
- nil odour (takes away the scent)
- no talking in zone.

Note there is some repetition in the zones detailed below, when comparing to those suggested for the mental health unit design, with minor adaptations added for this area.

Inspiring, creative zone

- inspiring art prints or pictures
- art materials, clay, beads, craft materials
- easels set up
- shelving with examples of things that can be made.

Music or auditory zone

- when in a large café or space, consider if there are areas where people can have more quiet e.g. speakers do not have to be in every area
- area for music
- music playing
- musical instruments

- space for dancing
- sound proofing or acoustic tiles.
- chair with headphones embedded in it.

TV zone

- soundproofing so that noise of television does not travel
- or headphones so that people who want to listen can tune in that way
- chairs spaced apart
- visual stimulation and changing lights of TV are managed so that they are not upsetting people who find this visual input disturbing

Eating zone

- space for those who would like to sit by self
- some social table arrangements
- choice of food tastes and textures
- management of acoustics through acoustic panels, chairs with felt bases, mats on floor (to minimise sound of scraping chairs
- consideration of strong smells (e.g. tuna) and ability to manage these.

Socialising zone

- area that is conducive to socialising
- chairs around tables and flexible seating arrangements possible to enable small groups
- shelving with board games
- background music should be low or not used (to assist people who have trouble filtering background sound
- arrange the space so that games invite people to join in e.g. giant jenga on the ground, indoor bowls.

Scent exploration zone

This area would ideally be outdoors as scent can be a trauma trigger for some people. If inside, it is preferable to use small sealable jars of scents including household and kitchen scents. These could be added to small individual pots for an individual kit. Plants may include herbs, scented flowers and leaves (e.g. geraniums) and fruit e.g. strawberries and citrus fruit.

Reading zone

- books, magazine, comfortable chairs
- bookcase with inspirational books, picture books, poetry, crossword or Sudoku books.

Reading zone

- comfortable chairs, cushions
- bookcase
- books, magazine, inspirational books, picture books, poetry, crossword or Sudoku

books.

Vegie patch

- patches would ideally promote digging or weeding as this would increase movement and proprioceptive input e.g. digging up sweet potatoes.

Icy zone

- small fridge with ice packs, icy balls, ice to suck, slushy drinks
- zip lock bags with cold water
- water drainage on floor
- non slip mats
- away from kids zone and noisy zones.

Game zone

- room set up for computer game use e.g. Wii, Nintendo
- headphones (wireless) may reduce noise levels.

Massage zone

- massage chair
- mini personal massagers
- massage table for visiting masseurs
- hand and body creams
- foot baths.

Shed zone

- woodwork equipment
- tools
- repairs.

Part 4

References and Index

Chapter 20:

References

References

Documents and educational excerpts:

Aina, T. (2009). *A guide to setting up a gym facility in a mental health unit*. National Health Service, United Kingdom. Retrieved from http://www.scmhforum.org.uk/documents/London_Development_Centre/Gym%20Guide_Final%20Version%20_2_.pdf

Australian Health Ministers' Advisory Council. (2013). *A national framework for recovery-oriented mental health services: A guide for practitioners and providers*. Canberra, Commonwealth of Australia. Retrieved from http://www.health.gov.au/internet/main/publishing.nsf/Content/67D17065514CF8E8CA257C1D00017A90/$File/recovgde.pdf

Berto, R. (2005). Exposure to restorative environments helps restore attentional capacity. *Journal of Environmental Psychology*. 25(3):249-259. DOI: 10.1371/journal.pone.0051474

Biel, L. (2006). *Welcoming special needs children at your library*. Paper presented at the American Library Association Annual Conference. Retrieved from http://www.rockingchairtherapy.org/autism.html

Brown, C & Dunn, W. (2002). Adolescent/Adult Sensory Profile. *Pearson Clinical*. www.pearsonclinical.com.au

Champagne, T. (2016). *OT innovations*. Retrieved from http://www.ot-innovations.com/

Dornan, C., Nowonty Lehsten, L., Woodin, M., Cohen. R., Schweitzer, J., & Trigilio Tona, J. (November 2009). Using sensory tools for teens. *OT Practice*, 16-21.Retrieved fromhttp://www.ateachabout.com/pdf/OTP_Nov09_UsingSensoryTools_Teens.pdf

Horticultural Society of NSW. *Sensory gardens* [Factsheet]. Retrieved from http://www.cultivatensw.org.au/imagesDB/wysiwyg/SensoryGardens.pdf

Lumb, B. (2014): comment on physiological society website on : 'Neural substrates underlying fear-evoked freezing: the periaqueductal grey - cerebellar link' by Stella Koutsikou, Jonathan J. Crook, Emma V. Earl, J. Lianne Leith, Thomas C. Watson, Bridget M. Lumb and Richard Apps (2014) in The Journal of Physiology. http://www.physoc.org/press-release/2014/unveiling-brain-circuits-involved-fear-response-gives-hope-panic-disorders-and-ph

Mental Health and Drug and Alcohol Office. (2015). *Safe use of sensory equipment and sensory rooms in NSW mental health services*. Ministry of Health, New South Wales, Australia. Retrieved from http://www1.health.nsw.gov.au/pds/ActivePDSDocuments/GL2015_001.pdf

Mental Health Standing Committee (2012). *2nd consultation draft national recovery-oriented mental health practice framework*: *The Trauma Informed Care Project 2015*. The Australian Health Ministers' Advisory Council, Australia. Retrieved from http://www.traumainformedcareproject.org/

Moore, K. (2006). *The sensory connection program*. Retrieved from http://www.sensoryconnectionprogram.com/senses.php

O'Hagan, M. (2006). The acute crisis: Towards a recovery plan for acute mental health services in New Zealand. Mental Health Commission, Wellington, N.Z.

O' Sullivan, J. and Fitzgibbon, C., (2018) *Sensory Modulation Brisbane* Retrieved from http://sensory-modulation-brisbane.com/sensory-modulation-blog/

Queensland Health (2008) Policy statement on reducing and where possible eliminating seclusion and restraint in Queensland mental health services. Brisbane, Australia, Mental Health Branch, Queensland Health.

SafeWards. (2017). *Equipment for calm down method box*. Retrieved fromhttp://www.safewards.net/images/pdf/Equipment_sources.pdf

Self Righting Star® (2012). *Enlightened Consultants*. Retrieved from: http://enlightened.com.au/ [Organisation name]

Siegal, D. (2011). *Daniel Siegal: Flipping your lid.* Retrieved from http://heartmindonline.org/resources/daniel-siegel-flipping-your-lid

TePou. (2017). *Sensory modulation as a suite of clinical tools in mental health settings* [Factsheet]. Retrieved from http://www.tepou.co.nz/uploads/files/resource-assets/Sensory-Modulation-As-a-Suite-of-Clinical-Tools-in-Mental-Health-Settings.pdf

Townsend, M., & Weerasuriya, R. (2010). *Beyond blue to green: The benefits of contact with nature for mental health and wellbeing*. Beyond Blue Ltd: Melbourne, Australia. Retrieved from http://www.deakin.edu.au/data/assets/pdf_file/0004/310747/Beyond-Blue-To-Green-Literature-Review.pdf

U.S. Department of Veterans Affairs. (2014). *Environmental programs service mental health guide.* Retrieved from https://www.patientsafety.va.gov/docs/joe/eps_mental_health_guide.pdf

Journal Articles and Texts:

Alcock, I; White, M; Wheeler, B; Fleming, L & Depledge, M. (2014). Longitudinal Effects on Mental Health of Moving to Greener and Less Green Urban Areas. *Environmental Science and Technology, 48* (2):1247-1255. DOI: 10.1021/es403688w

Anthony, W. (1993). Recovery from mental illness: The guiding vision of the mental health service system in the 1990s. *Psychosocial Rehabilitation Journal, 16*(4), 11-23.

Bayer, L., Constantinescu, I., Perrig, S., Vienne, J., Vidal, P., Muhlethaler, M., & Schwartz, S. (2011). Rocking synchronises brain waves during a short nap. *Current Biology, 21*, 1-12.

Bialer, D. S., and L. J. Miller. (2011). No Longer A SECRET: Unique Common Sense Strategies for Children with Sensory or Motor Challenges. Arlington, TX: Sensory World.

Blackman, J. (2017). Welcome to Parent-infant disturbance: Theory and therapy. *Journal of International Forum of Psychoanalysis, 26*(1):8-9.http://dx.doi.org/10.1080/0803706X.2016.1195514

Bratman, G., Daily, G., Ley, B., Gross, J. (2015). The benefits of nature experience: Improved affect and cognition. *Landscape and Urban Planning, 138*, 41-50. Retrieved from http://spl.stanford.edu/pdfs/2015/Bratman%20LUP.pdf

Brown, C., Cromwell, R., Filion, D., Dunn, W., & Tollefson, N. (2002). Sensory processing in schizophrenia: Missing and avoiding information. *Schizophrenia Research, 55*, 187-195.

Brown, C., Tollefson, N., Dunn, W., Cromwell, R., & Filion, D. (2001). The adult sensory profile: Measuring patterns of sensory processing. *American Journal of Occupational Therapy, 55*(1), 75-82.

Buccheri, R.K., Trygstad, L.N., Buffum, M.D., Lyttle, K., & Dowling, G. (2010). Comprehensive evidence-based program teaching self-management of auditory hallucinations on inpatient psychiatric units. *Issues in Mental Health Nursing, 31*(3), 223-231. doi:10.3109/01612840903288568

Bushman, B. J. (2002). Does venting anger feed or extinguish the flame? Catharsis, rumination, distraction, anger, and aggressive responding. *Personality and Social Psychology Bulletin, 28*, 724-731.doi:10.1177/0146167202289002

Cameron, O.G. (2001). Interoception: The Inside Story - A Model for Psychosomatic Processes. Psychosomatic Medicine, 63, 697-710.

Chalmers, C., Harrison, S., Mollison, K., Molloy, N., & Gray, K. (2012). Establishing sensory-based approaches in mental health inpatient care: A multidisciplinary approach. *Australasian Psychiatry, 20*(1), 35-39.

Champagne, T. (2006). Creating sensory rooms: Environmental enhancements for acute inpatient mental health settings. *Mental Health Special Interest Section Quarterly, 28*, 1-4.

Champagne, T. (2011). *Sensory modulation & environment: Essential elements of occupation* (3rd ed. revised). Australia: Pearson.

Champagne, T., Koomar, J., & Olson, L. (2010). Sensory processing evaluation and intervention in mental health. *OT Practice, 15*(5):1-8.

Dunn, W (2001). The Sensations of Everyday Life: Empirical, Theoretical, and Pragmatic Considerations, *The American Journal of Occupational Therapy*, 55(6):608-620.

Dunn, W (2007). Supporting Children to Partipate Successfully in Everyday Life by Using Sensory Processing Knowledge. *Infants and Young Children*, 20 (2) pp 84-101.

Hofer, M. K., Collins, H.K., Whillans, A. V, Chen, F, S., (2018) Olfactory cues from romantic partners and strangers influence women's responses to stress. *Journal of Personality and Social Psychology*. doi:10.1037/pspa0000110

Champagne, T., Mullen, B., Dickson, D., & Krishnamurty, S. (2015). Evaluating the safety and effectiveness of the weighted blanket with adults during an inpatient mental health hospitalization. *Occupational Therapy in Mental Health, 31*(3):211-233.

Champagne, T., & Stromberg, N. (2004). Sensory approaches in inpatient psychiatric settings: Innovative alternatives to seclusion and restraint. *Journal of Psychosocial Nursing, 42*(9), 1-8. Retrieved from http://www.mass.gov/eohhs/docs/dmh/rsri/sensory-article.pdf

Chaudhury, H. (2004). Critical Advances in Reminiscence Work: From Theory to Application. *Canadian Journal on Aging*. 23(2):193-194.

Cloitre, M., Koenen, K.C., Cohen, L.R., Han, H. (2002) Skills training in affective and interpersonal regulation followed by exposure: a phase-based treatment for PTSD related to childhood abuse. *Journal of consulting and clinical psychology: 70* (5): 1067-1074

Cook, J., Copeland M. E., Hamilton, M., Jonikas, J., Razzano, L., Floyd, C., Hudson, W., Macfarlane, R., & Grey, D. (2009). Initial outcomes of a mental illness self-management program based on wellness recovery action planning. *Psychiatric Services, 60*(2), 246-247.

Crepaz-Keay, D. (2010, October). *Self-management of mental health problems*. Paper presented at World Health Organisation and European Commission Meeting on Empowerment in Mental Health: Working together towards leadership, Leuven, Belgium.

Dunn, B., Stefanovitch, I., Evans, D., Oliver, C., Hawkings, A., & Dalgleish, T. (2010). Can you feel the beat? Interoceptive awareness is an interactive function of anxiety- and depression-specific symptom dimensions. *Behaviour, Research, Therapy, 48*(11), 1133-1138. doi:10.1016/j.brat.2010.07.006

Dunn, W. (2001) The sensations of everyday life: Empirical, theoretical, and pragmatic considerations. American Journal of Occupational Therapy, 55, 608-620

Dunn, W (2007). Supporting Children to Partipate Successfully in Everyday Life by Using Sensory Processing Knowledge. *Infants and Young Children*, 20 (2) pp 84-101

Dunn, W. (2013). *Living sensationally*. London: Jessica King Publishers.

Faber Taylor, A & Ming Kuo, F. (2011). Could Exposure to Everyday Green Spaces Help Treat ADHD Evidence from Children's Play Settings. *Applied Psychology: Health and Well-Being*, 3(3): 281-303. DOI: 10.1111/j.1758-0854.2011.01052.x

Farmaki, C., Sakkalis, V., Gjini, K., Boutros, N., & Zouridakis, G. (2014). Assessment of sensory gating deficit in schizophrenia using a wavelet transform methodology on auditory paired-click evoked potentials. *Modern Electorencephalographic Assessment Techniques, 91*, 205-229. Retrieved from https://doi.org/10.1007/7657_2014_71

Fitzgibbon, C., & O'Sullivan, J., (2013). Sensory Strategies as Standard Practice: an OT initiative to embed sensory approaches into public sector mental health services, *14th International Mental Health Conference book of proceedings and conference papers.*

O'Sullivan, J., Fitzgibbon, C. (2014) Integrating Sensory Approaches into OT Mental Health Practice: Adopting a Sensory Lens to Enhance Functional Outcomes, *OT Australia Sensory Approaches Series.*

Fitzgibbon, C., & O'Sullivan, J.(2015). Sensory Approaches, *Sensory Approaches In-service Series,* Headspace Woollongabba.

Fitzgibbon, C., O Sullivan, J (2017). Supporting Our Sensory Systems (SOSs) *Sensory Training Workshops, Penrith.*

Fosha, D., Siegel, D.J., & Solomon, M.F. (2009). The healing power of emotion: Affective neuroscience, development and clinical practice. New York: Norton.

Frumkin, M. (2001). Beyond toxicity: Human health and the natural environment. *American Journal of Preventative Medicine,* 20(3):234-240. https://doi.org/10.1016/S0749-3797(00)00317-2

Glover, H. (2012). Recovery, lifelong learning, social inclusion and empowerment: Is a new paradigm emerging?InP. Ryan, S. Ramon, & T. Greacen (Eds.), *Empowerment, lifelong learning and recovery in mental health: towards a new paradigm* (pp.15-35). Victoria: Palgrave Publishers.

Gay, J. (2012). *Positive solutions in practice: using sensory focused activities to help* reduce restraint and seclusion. Melbourne, Victorian Government Department of Human Services.

Gonzalez, M & Kirkevold, M. (2014). Clinical Use of Sensory Gardens and Outdoor Environments in Norwegian Nursing Homes: A Cross-Sectional E-mail Survey. *Issues in Mental Health Nursing* , 36(1):35-43. http://dx.doi.org/10.3109/01612840.2014.932872

Grahn, P & Stigsdotter, U. (2003). Landscape planning and stress. *Urban Forestry and Urban Greening,* 2:1-18.

Grandin, T. (1992). Calming effects of deep touch pressure in patients with autistic disorder, college students and animals. *Journal of Child and Adolescent Psychopharmacology, 2*(1). Retrieved from http://www.grandin.com/inc/squeeze.html

Hartig, T; Evans, G; Jamner, L; Davis, D; and Gärling, T. (2003). Tracking restoration in natural and urban field settings. *Journal of Environmental Psychology* 23:109–123.http://dx.doi.org/10.1016/S0272-4944 (02)00109-3

Hartman, D. (2017). Beating anxiety: What young people on the autism spectrum need to know. London: Jessica Kingsley Publishers.

Hirano, Y. & Onozuka, M. (2015). Chewing and attention: A positive effect on sustained attention. *Biomedical Research* International, 1-6. Retrieved fromhttp://dx.doi.org/10.1155/2015/367026

Hockenbury, D.H., & Hockenbury, S.E. (2007). *Discovering Psychology*. (4thed.). New York: Worth Publishers, Inc.

Holt-Damant, K., Guaralda, M., Taylor Gomez, M., & Nicollet, C. (2013, June). *Urban jungle: Making cities healthy places for Australians with neurodiversity*. Paper presented at the 6thMaking Cities Liveable Conference (in conjunction with Sustainable Transformation Conference), Melbourne. Retrieved from http://www.academia.edu/4322127/Urban_jungle_making_cities_healthy_places_for_Australians_with_neurodiversity

Huckshorn, K.A. (2006). Redesigning state mental health policy to prevent the use of seclusion and restraint. *Administration and Policy in Mental Health and Mental Health Services Research*, 33 (4), 482-491.

Jacobson, N. & Greenley, D. (2001). What is recovery? A conceptual model and explication. *Psychiatric Services, 52*, 482-485. Retrieved from http://www.state.sc.us/dmh/recovery_training.htm

Kaplan, R. & Kaplan, S. (1989) The Experience of Nature: A Psychological Perspective. Cambridge University Press, New York.

Kaiser, E., Gillette, C., & Spinazzola, J. (2010). A controlled pilot-outcome study of sensory integration (SI) in the treatment of complex adaptation to traumatic stress. *Journal of Aggression, Maltreatment and Trauma, 19*,699-720. Retrieved from http://www.traumacenter.org/products/pdf_files/SI%20Txt%20for%20Adult%20Complex%20PTSD%20article-Spinazzola.pdf

Koomar, J., Warner, E., & Westcott, A. (2009). *Arousal regulation in traumatised children - sensorimotor interventions.* Presentation at International Trauma Conference, Boston Ma. Retrieved from http://www.traumacenter.org/announcements/TConf.09_SMART_Handouts.pdf

Korpela, K., Hartig, T., Kaiser, F., Fuhrer, U. (2001). Restorative Experience and Self-Regulation in Favourite Places. Environment and Behaviour. 33. 10.1177/00139160121973133.

Koutsikou, S; Crook, J J; Earl, E V; Leith, J L; Watson, T C; Lumb, B M & Apps, R (2014). Neural substrates underlying fear-evoked freezing: the periaqueductal grey - cerebellar link. *Journal of Physiology, 15, 2197-213. doi:* 10.1113/jphysiol.2013.268714

Kuhaneck, H.M., & Kelleher, J. (2015). Development of the classroom sensory environment assessment (CSEA). *American Journal of Occupational Therapy, 69:1-9.*

Melzack, R. & Wall, P. (1965). Pain mechanisms: a new theory. *Science, New Series*, Vol 150 (3699): 971-979 doi:10.5014/ajot.2015.019430

Mullen, B; Champagne, T; Krishnamurty, S; Dickson, D & Gao, R. (2008). Exploring the Safety and Therapeutic Effects of Deep Pressure Stimulation Using a Weighted Blanket, 24(1): 65-89. http://dx.doi.org/10.1300/J004v24n01_05

Lanius, U.F., Paulsen, S.L., & Corrigan, F.M. (2014). *Neurobiology and treatment of traumatic dissociation: Towards an embodied self.* New York: Springer Publishing.

Law, M., Cooper, B., Strong, S., Stewart, D., Rigby, P., & Letts, L. (1996) The Person-Environment-Occupation Model: A transactive approach to occupational performance. *Canadian Journal of Occupational Therapy*, *63*(1):9-23. doi:10.1177/000841749063OO103

LeBel, J., Champagne, T., Stromberg, N., & Coyle, R. (2010). Integrating sensory and trauma-informed interventions: A Massachusetts state initiative, part 1. *Mental Health Special Interest Section Quarterly*, 33(1), 1-4.

Lee, S. J., Cox, A., Whitecross, F., Williams, P., & Hollander, Y. (2010). Sensory assessment and therapy to help reduce seclusion use with service users needing psychiatric intensive care. *Journal of Psychiatric Intensive Care*, 6:83-90. doi:10.1017/S1742646410000014

Linehan, M. (2015). *DBT skills training manual* (2nd ed.). New York: The Guilford Press.

Lloyd, C., King, R., & Machingura, T. (2014). An investigation into the effectiveness of sensory modulation in reducing seclusion within an acute mental health unit. *Advances in Mental Health: promotion, prevention and early intervention*, *12*(2), 93–100

Lorig, KR & Holman, H. (2003). Self-management education: History, definitions, outcomes and mechanisms. *Annals of Behavioural Medicine*, 26(1):1-7.

Mathics, C., & Bannister, R. (2013). Autonomic failure: A textbook of clinical disorders of the autonomic nervous system. London: Oxford University Press.

McGee, M. (2012). Neurodiversity. *Contexts*, *11*(3), 12–13. Retrieved from http://journals.sagepub.com/doi/pdf/10.1177/1536504212456175

Middleton Centre for Autism. (2015). *Sensory Audit*. Retrieved at http://sensory-processing.middletownautism.com/sensory-strategies/sensory-audit-for-school-and-classrooms/

Miller, A.L., Rathus, J.H., & Linehan, M.M. (2012). *Dialectical behavior therapy with suicidal adolescents*. New York: The Guilford Press.

Miller, L. J., Reisman, J. E., McIntosh, D. N., & Simon, J. (2001). An ecological model of sensory modulation. In S. Smith Roley, E. Blanche, & R. C. Schaaf (Eds.), *Understanding the nature of sensory integration with diverse populations* (pp. 57–82). San Antonio, TX: Therapy Skill Builders.

Moore, K. (2016). *Sensory connection program curriculum for self-regulation* [Factsheet]. Retrieved fromhttp://www.sensoryconnectionprogram.com/curriculum_overview.pdf

Mullen, B., Champagne, T., Krishnamurthy, S., Dickson, D., & Gao, R. (2008). Evaluating the safety and effectiveness of the weighted blanket with adults during an inpatient mental health hospitalization. *Occupational Therapy in Mental Health*, *24*(1), 65–89. Retrieved from http://www.tandfonline.com/doi/abs/10.1080/0164212X.2015.1066220?journalCode=womh20

Nutsford, D; Pearson, A; Kingham, S & Reitma, F. (2016). Residential exposure to visible blue space (but not green space) associated with lower psychological distress in a capital city. *Health and Place,* 39(5):70-78. Retrieved from https://doi.org/10.1016/j.healthplace.2016.03.002

Ogden, P., Pain, C., & Fisher, J. (2006). A sensorimotor approach to the treatment of trauma and dissociation. *Psychiatric Clinics of North America*, *29*, 263- 279. Retrieved from http://psychrights.org/Research/Digest/CriticalThinkRxCites/ogden.pdf

Omlin, X., Crivelli, F., Heinicke, L., Zaunsede, S., Achermann, P., & Riener R. (2016.) Effect of rocking movements on respiration. *PLoS ONE*,*11*(3). Retrieved from http://journals.plos.org/plosone/article?id=10.1371/journal.pone.0150581

Pacciardi, B., Mauri, M., Cargioli, C., Belli, S., Cotugno, B., Di Paolo, L., & Pini, S. (2013). Issues in the management of acute agitation: how much current guidelines consider safety? *Frontiers in Psychiatry,* 4(26):1-10 DOI: 10.3389/fpsyt.2013.00026

Phillips, R., Hewedi, D., Eissa, A., Moustafa, A (2015) The Cerebellum and Psychiatric Disorders. *Frontiers in Public Health, 3: 66 doi:* 10.3389/fpubh.2015.00066

Porges, S. W. (2011). The Polyvagal Theory: Phylogenetic substrates of a social nervous system. *International Journal of Psychophysiology, 42,* 123-146. http://dx.doi.org/10.1016/S0167-8760(01)00162-3

Randal, P., Stewart, M.W., Proverbs, D., Lampshire, D., Symes, J., & Hamer, H. (2009). The Recovery Model – An integrative developmental stress-vulnerability-strengths approach to mental health. *Psychosis*, 1(2)122–133. doi:10.1080/17522430902948167

Reynolds, S., Lane.S., & Mullen, B. (2015). Effects of Deep Pressure Stimulation on physiological arousal. *The American Journal of Occupational Therapy*, 69(3), 1-10. doi:10.5014/ajot.2015.015560

Rothschild, B. (2010). *8 keys to safe trauma recovery*. New York: Norton Professional.

Rothschild, B. (2011). *Trauma essentials*. New York: Norton Professional.

Rudd, M., Aaker, J., & Vohs, K. (2012). Awe expands people's perception of time, alters decision making, and enhances well-being. *Psychological Science*, *23*(10), 1130-1136. Retrieved from http://www.bauer.uh.edu/mrrudd/download/AweExpandsTimeAvailability.pdf

Schuch, B., Vancampfort, D., Richards, J., Rosenbarum, S., Ward, P., & Stubbs, B. (2016). Exercise as a treatment for depression: A meta-analysis adjusting for publication bias. *Journal of Psychiatric Research*, *77*, 42-51. Retrieved from http://www.sciencedirect.com/science/article/pii/S0022395616300383

Schulz, A., Vogele, C. Interoception and Stress, (2015) *Frontiers Psychology*6: 993. doi: 10.3389/fpsyg.2015.00993

Shepherd, G., Boardman, J., & Slade, M. (2008). *Making recovery a reality*. London, Sainsbury Centre for Mental Health. Retrieved from https://www.centreformentalhealth.org.uk/Handlers/Download.ashx?IDMF=e94d8999-4010-4a5e-a5d8-0c3f1eb2d0e6

Siegel, DJ. (1999) The Developing Mind: Toward a Neurobiology of Interpersonal Experience. New York: Guilford Press.

Speer, M. E., Bhanji, J.P., Delgado, M.R., (2014). Savoring the past: Positive memories evoke value representations in the striatum. *Neuron*, 84 (4): 847-856

Stonerock, G., Hoffman, B., Smith, P., & Blumenthal, J. (2015). Exercise as treatment for anxiety: Systematic review and analysis. *Annals of Behavioural, Medicine*, *49*(4), 542–556. doi: 10.1007/s12160-014-9685-9

Strata, P. (2015). The Emotional Cerebellum. *The Cerebellum (on line journal)*: Springer Science: 1-8. DOI: 10.1007/s12311-015-0649-9.

Sutton, D., & Nicholson, E. (2011). *Sensory modulation in acute mental health wards: A qualitative study of staff and service user perspectives*. Auckland, New Zealand: TePou o TeWhakaaro Nui. Retrieved from http://aut.researchgateway.ac.nz/bitstream/handle/10292/4312/Sutton%20sensory%20modulation%20in%20acute%20mental%20health%20wards.pdf?sequence=6

Taylor, AG; Goehler, LE; Galper, DI; Innes, KE & Bourguignon, C. (2010). Top-Down and Bottom-Up Mechanisms in Mind-Body Medicine: Development of an Integrative Framework for Psychophysiological Research. *The Journal of Science and Healing,* 6(1):29-41. https://doi.org/10.1016/j.explore.2009.10.004

Townsend, M., & Weerasuriya, R. (2010). *Beyond blue to green: The benefits of contact with nature for mental health and wellbeing*. Beyond Blue Ltd: Melbourne, Australia. Retrieved from http://www.deakin.edu.au/__data/assets/pdf_file/0004/310747/Beyond-Blue-To-Green-Literature-Review.pdf

Trost, W.J., Labbe, C., & Grandjean, D. (2017). Rhythmic entrainment as a musical affect induction mechanism. *Neuropsychologia,96*, 96–110.Retrieved from http://cms2.unige.ch/fapse/neuroemo/pdf/Trost,%20Labbé%20&%20Grandjean%20(2017)%20Rhythmic%20entrainment%20as%20a%20musical%20affect%20induction%20mechanism.pdf

Ulrich, R.S (1981). Natural versus urban scenes: Some psychophysiological effects. *Environment and Behaviour,* 13(5):523-556.https://doi.org/10.1177/0013916581135001

Ulrich, R; Simons, R; Losito, B; Fiorito, E; Miles, M & Zelson, M. (1991). Stress recovery during exposure to natural and urban environments. *Journal of Environmental Psychology,* 11(3):201-230.https://doi.org/10.1016/S0272-4944(05)80184-7

Van Der Kolk, B. (2006). Clinical implications of neuroscience research in PTSD.*Annals of the New York Academy of Sciences*, 1–17. Retrieved from http://www.traumacenter.org/products/pdf_files/NYASF.pdf

Van Der Kolk, B., Stone, L., West, J., Rhodes, A., Emerson, D., Suvak, M., & Spinazzola, J. (2014). Yoga as an adjunct treatment for posttraumatic stress disorder: A randomized controlled trial. *Journal of Clinical Psychiatry, 75*, 1–7. Retrieved from http://www.traumacenter.org/products/pdf_files/Yoga_Adjunctive_Treatment_PTSD_V0001.pdf

Velarde, M; Fry, G & Tveit. (2007). Health effects of viewing landscapes – Landscape types in environmental psychology. *Urban Forestry & Urban Greening,* 6(4):199-212. Retrieved from https://doi.org/10.1016/j.ufug.2007.07.001

Watson, N., Wells, T., & Cox, C. (1998). Rocking chair therapy for dementia patients: Its effect on psychosocial wellbeing and balance. *American Journal of Alzheimer's Disease and other Dementias, 13*(6), 296–308.Retrieved from https://doi.org/10.1177/153331759801300605

Weinstein, A. D. (2016). Prenatal development and parents' lived experiences: How early events shape our psychophysiology and relationships (Norton Series on Interpersonal Neurobiology). New York: Norton Publishing.

White, C.M. (2011). Self-management: A close companion to recovery in mental illness. *Occupational Therapy Now, 13*(5), 26–27.

Wiebkng, C & Northoff, G. (2014). Interoceptive Awareness of the Insula: Application of Neuroimaging Techniques in Psychotherapy. *International Journal of Psychiatry,* 1(1):53-60. DOI:10.5176/0000-0002_1.1.8

Wilbarger P and Wilbarger J. (1997) Sensory defensiveness and related social/emotional and neurological problems. VanNuys, CA:Wilbarger.

Wolf, H. (2011). Self-management and mental health (Chapter 22). In S. Bährer-Kohler (Ed) *Social Determinants and Mental Health*. New York: Nova Science Publishing Inc. Retrieved from http://www.researchgate.net/profile/Henrike_Wolf/publication/215678736_SELF-MANAGEMENT_AND_MENTAL_HEALTH/links/0fcfd506ca8b7170d3000000.pdf

Chapter 21:

Index

Biography

Julie O'Sullivan and Carolyn Fitzgibbon are experienced mental health clinicians and occupational therapists. They have used sensory modulation in their clinical work and in designing sensory spaces, and find that many clients find it practical, and easy to use. Julie and Carolyn have spoken with many clinicians, teachers and support workers who wanted to use sensory modulation but were unsure of how to get started. This book was written in response to this need, to provide a practical guide to help people learn more about sensory modulation and how to best utilise the strategies to enhance client functioning, wellbeing and quality of life.

More information on Sensory Modulation Brisbane

Facebook.com/sensorymod/

Pinterest.com.au/SensoryMod/

LinkedIn: Carolyn Fitzgibbon

LinkedIn: Julie O' Sullivan

www. sensory-modulation-brisbane.com/

www.dbtbrisbane.com.au

Review

Thankyou for reading

We invite you to post a review of this book on the site that you purchased it from.

Printed in the USA
CPSIA information can be obtained
at www.ICGtesting.com
LVHW010400301023
762449LV00012BA/1322